THE CHRISTIAN MESSAGE IN A SCIENTIFIC AGE

The
CHRISTIAN MESSAGE
in a
SCIENTIFIC AGE

Albert N. Wells

JOHN KNOX PRESS
Richmond, Virginia

Library of Congress Catalog Card Number: 62-19483

To that growing company of contemporary Christians who feel themselves constrained by their commitment to Jesus Christ to strive in all of life to "think God's thoughts after him."

Preface

Many years ago James Denney began a series of lectures to an audience of theological students by stating his aim to be "to help you to be true to all you know, and at the same time to keep a complete and joyful faith as Christian men." Within the setting of a modern scientific culture Christian theology cannot afford to have any less an aim than this if it is to fulfill its responsibility. Traditionally, we have thought of the theologian and the natural scientist as being two different people, and the difficulty lay in bringing about a satisfactory *rapprochement* between them. But time has long since shown this to be too simple a characterization of the situation.

No doubt the problem still exists in its older form, but in the modern world a man must be able to be a theologian (either professional or lay, it does not matter) and a scientist *at the same time.* He must be able to regard the world from the biblical point of view as God's world and yet also assimilate into his thinking the sound insights of modern science. Conversely, if he is a man of science he will need—as a man, at the very least—to be able to accept a vantage point within history and yet above and unconditioned by it so that he may achieve that measure of wholeness and meaning necessary for real sanity.

These pages are written in the conviction that when the thoughtful Christian avails himself of the up-to-date knowledge about physical reality that is available today, he is likely to sense immediately that physical reality, in both its very large and its very small dimensions, displays essentially the very character it must display to be the reality which the God of the Bible created and continues to sustain.

7

To present the information that natural science supplies about the physical world against the background in history of this modern understanding, and then to show how this knowledge actually contributes to our understanding of the biblical revelation of God and his will: This is our aim. It is the aim of one who believes that when we consider the convictions of Christian theology and the findings of natural science together, they lead us in the direction of wholeness rather than to the "warfare" that has traditionally been associated with this relationship.

It would be an utter impossibility to make adequate acknowledgment of those who by their kind and patient assistance have contributed to the writing of these pages. As I look back, I am deeply sensitive of the profound debt of gratitude which I owe to so many. Without mentioning any specifically for fear of omitting others inadvertently, let me direct this simple but sincere word of thanks to all whose partnership I have received in this endeavor. "I thank my God in all my remembrance of you . . ."

ALBERT N. WELLS

Contents

Part One

THE PHYSICAL CHARACTER
OF HUMAN EXPERIENCE

Chapter I

The Scientific Apprehension of Reality

The most immediate content of human experience is physical in character. Reality, as we know it, would be quite inconceivable without the physical. We encounter physical reality in an almost infinite variety of expressions and arrangements during the course of a normal day. Living creatures, the life of the mind, and the life of the spirit bring into view new dimensions other than the physical, but we meet them only in connection with some physical body. Life and consciousness are both embedded in the physical. When a child first awakens to consciousness, it sees things as objects only. The plastic toy, the crib, its own toes—these are the realities that help to introduce the child to the world. Even when he comes to regard himself and his mother as subjects rather than objects, he is aware that these subjects are never encountered apart from a physical form. The omnipresence of matter is an elemental fact of existence. We are encompassed by it.

It is not surprising, therefore, that one of man's oldest recorded questions is "Of what is physical reality made?"[1] A simple, unsophisticated inquiry indeed, so it seems to us. But in this world the answers to even the simplest questions have a way of being elusive. This is, in fact, a large part of the never-ending fascination of scientific research. Science is a kind of master detective story involving hundreds of "special agents" striving to work out the patterns of the "clues" which seem best to fit the facts. When fresh information is uncovered through mathematics or experimentation, making current answers obsolete, then new solutions must be devised. Here and there great creative spirits dominate the landscape by their ability to envision and formulate the master answers which explain and account for the largest number of "clues" in any given situation. Sometimes "false leads" and "blind alleys" develop and persist for centuries until a more adequate solution is formulated and put to the test extensively enough to be accepted over prevailing opinion. Science is an unwearying process of criticism and correction, and the story of man's search for the answer to the above question is an excellent illustration of it.

Even after two and one half millenia it is not possible to give an outright, unequivocal answer. In fact, it is recognized that to do so would be inimical to true science. Yet at the same time, the end result of scientific search can hardly be said to be inconclusive. Science has arrived at that point in its development where it can give an intelligible, meaningful reply, and it is clear that it approximates the truth far closer than any previous solution. Yet it is the kind of answer which actually deepens the sense of mystery that surrounds even the most elementary things. There is enough permanence in it for us to be satisfied concerning its validity; there is enough contingency in it to leave room for future modification. Most important of all for the Christian, what science says about physical reality today strikes a responsive chord when we consider it in relation to the biblical view of the world.

During practically his entire recorded history man has lived with the illusion that physical reality has a firm, substantial character. Objects, the earth itself, his own body—these seemed solid enough to one who early found his sense impressions for the most part to be trustworthy and who therefore did not feel the need for inquiring beyond the data they supply.

Antiquity's foremost natural philosopher assumed that matter has an inert, massive quality, and affirmed that it is only by the intervention of some kind of form that it assumes the various shapes that appear. It was Aristotle's fundamental conviction that reality is intelligible and that the character of its intelligibility can in every case be determined within reality itself. It is well known that Aristotle was an empirical philosopher and that his empiricism was a valuable correction of his master Plato who taught that the correct approach to truth is introspective.

Unlike Plato, Aristotle envisioned physical reality in the shape of a regularly and evenly ascending hierarchy of matter—to be exact, from inert or "formless" matter up to the very peak of "matterless form." Within this type of situation it can be seen that the task of the physical scientist is that of a cataloguer. He ranges up and down the various expressions of physical reality, endeavoring to "describe" them adequately and to determine their "purpose" within the setting of the whole.

While at first glance it might appear that Aristotle was more scientific than Plato, as matters actually turned out, he was much less so. The empirical point of view is not necessarily the scientific point of view. It is not at all unfair to say that Aristotle was more interested in the forms in which matter appears than he was in matter itself. The *intellectual formulation* of physical reality was for him of greater importance than the *nature* of physical reality. The real thrust of his work in physics therefore lay in cataloguing rather than in experimenting and utilizing. Having compiled the rational categories into which reality is supposed to fit, there remained nothing for the scientist of Aristotelian inspiration to do but to range over the whole of the physical order assigning things to their proper place. Not physical reality itself, but the metaphysical categories in which it can be catalogued and comprehended —this comfortable but enslaving scheme of things came in time to be seen as the true Aristotelian legacy in science.

Aristotle's elaborate metaphysical scheme dominated the landscape of science for a millenium and a half. It seemed adequate, so why inquire further? To be sure, there were other more promising interpretations of physical reality than this. Thales had propounded the thesis that the fundamental stuff of the physical order is water, Anaximander that it was air, Anaximenes that it was *apeiron*, the "boundless." These suggestions seem almost primitive to us, it is true, but they at least had the merit of encouraging further research and actual experimentation. The most "modern" of the ancient views was that of Democritus and Leucippus who stated that physical reality consists of atoms or grains of matter ceaselessly moving about in space. These "atomists" thus formulated a kind of atomic theory two and one half thousand years before Max Planck. But the logical appeal and comprehensiveness of the Aristotelian metaphysics won the field, and these more fertile leads—along with the pioneering spirit of true experimental science—were left unexplored. As Francis Bacon succinctly puts it in a classic passage:

> The common notion of the falling off of the old systems upon the publication of Aristotle's works is a false one; for long afterward, down even to the times of Cicero and subsequent ages, the works of the old philosophers [i.e., the early cosmologists and atomists] still remained. But in the times which followed, when on the inundation of barbarians into the Roman empire human learning had suffered shipwreck, then the systems of Aristotle and Plato, like planks of lighter and less solid material, floated on the waves of time, and were preserved.[2]

Among other things, the "shipwreck" of human learning meant that the authority of Aristotle as *the* philosopher of physical reality loomed even larger, and the advent of true science postponed until a future emancipation.

When that emancipation began in the fourteenth and fifteenth centuries, it assumed the form of an utter repudiation of the Aristotelian methodology in science, particularly as that methodology had become enshrined in the *Summae* of Thomas Aquinas. Experiment and mathematics—these were now seen to be the fundamental constituents of the search to unlock the secrets of the natural order, not rational categorization. Plato had indeed insisted on the importance of mathematics (though Aristotle had not). But for Plato mathematics was a philosophical discipline; its value lay in the fact that it trained the mind to discern and envision the pure ideas which he considered to be the archetypes of all things. This seems to have been in general the ancient Greek view of mathematics; it may explain in part why Aristotle rejected it—he saw it as part and parcel of Plato's introspective approach. Not until the beginning of the modern era was the intimate relationship between mathematics and the existing physical order understood. Thus with the clearer conception of mathematics the foundations of modern science were laid and the way opened to the understanding of the true structure of physical reality.

This new approach proved itself during the seventeenth century, the "century of genius," when those engaged in the study of the nature of physical reality in effect went back and began all over again. Gassendi reinstated the basic doctrine of the atomists, suggesting that everything in reality is composed of rigid and indestructible particles, similar in substance but different in size and form, moving about in all directions through space.[3] A few years later Robert Boyle, developing this idea further, laid the foundations of modern chemistry with the conception of the chemical element. Physical reality came to be understood in terms of different *elements* of matter, the particles or "building blocks" of each element having their own characteristic shape and qualities. The "incomparable" Sir Isaac Newton supplied the capstone of the new view by interpreting the relation between atoms or particles in terms of mutual attraction.

> Now the smallest Particles of Matter may cohere by the strongest Attractions, and compose bigger Particles of weaker Virtue, and many of these may cohere and compose bigger Particles whose Virtue is weaker still, and so on for divers Successions. . . . If the Body is compact, and bends or yields inward to Pression without sliding of its Parts, it is hard and elastic, returning to its Figure with a Force rising from the mutual Attraction of its Parts.[4]

Thus in place of the metaphysical approach to the understanding of physical reality there was substituted a mechanical view based on mathematical formulation. Matter was now regarded as consisting of atoms causally related to each other, the strength of the attraction or repulsion being ascertainable by the simple application of Newton's inverse square law of universal gravitation.[5]

This mechanical view of physical reality was without doubt a tremendous advance. Its success can be traced to the fact that in it science discovered a system of laws which applied quite well to objects of moderate size. Movement of a rectangular block down an inclined plane, the pressure of gases within a closed cylinder, the movements of the planets within the solar system—all these could be accounted for with ample adequacy by the mechanical explanation. In this scheme of things, reality was considered to be governed by mechanistic laws, the future determined completely by the past. Furthermore, it was assumed that these basic physical principles would vindicate themselves on every level of investigation and discovery. So successful was the mechanical view, in fact, that it seemed highly unlikely that any important change would ever have to be made in the fundamental mechanical assumptions on which it operated.

> It was hard to imagine the physicists of the future finding any more exciting occupation than dotting the i's and crossing the t's of the mechanical explanation of the universe, and carrying the measurement of the physical quantities to further decimal places.[6]

The fact that things did not work out this way is known to every person familiar with the course of scientific events since the last quarter of the nineteenth century. As long as medium-sized objects were under consideration, the Newtonian explanation seemed to be almost entirely satisfactory. But further research into the dimensions of the very large and the very small disclosed data that did not fit the mechanistic formulation. Atoms and molecules simply refused to behave according to the principles of Newtonian mechanics, and their failure to do so was radical and fundamental. Nor was it a failure in accuracy or in degree of precision. The discovery of electromagnetism by James Clerk Maxwell was the first definite experimental confirmation that something was wrong. Somewhat later the discovery of radioactivity and the various types of rays emitted from within the structure of certain elements showed that the Newtonian view of the structure of matter was far too simple. Clearly some sort of motion was involved which was not mechanical in character, and the facts pointed to the need for radical correction.

To make short the rather lengthy but exciting story of the development of the theory of atomic structure in the last eighty-five years, physicists found that matter is composed of electrons as well as atoms, infinitesimally minute charged particles revolving with unbelievable speed about a central nucleus. The "planetary" view of atomic structure came into being: a central nucleus in which the mass of the atom is concentrated, with one or more electrons whirling around it like planets in solar orbits. An entirely new category, that of electrical charge, was thus added to the nomenclature of physical reality. It was now recognized that physical reality has not only mass but energy. More than this, in what is easily the most spectacular development of modern science, mass and energy are interchangeable, the basis of this interchangeability being Einstein's famous formula, $E = Mc^2$, where the constant c represents the velocity of light. An infinitesimal quantity of mass convertible into an enormous release of energy: This is the new and bizarre principle which forms the very cornerstone of modern atomic physics.

These developments have made it abundantly clear that physical reality is far more complex than ever could have been imagined under either the metaphysical or the mechanical system of interpreting it. Gone is the simple "building block" universe of Newtonian days. So rapid has been the growth of understanding regarding atomic structure that even the "planetary" view referred to above and familiar to freshman physics classes must be used with definite reservations. For example, instead of a single electron revolving around a central hydrogen nucleus, a "whole plethora of evanescent particles" has been detected.[7] At the same time, an accurate picture of the structure of the atom is impossible to secure. According to the Heisenberg principle of indeterminacy, it is impossible to determine both an electron's position and its velocity simultaneously. And the same holds true for other particles as well. In fact it is only in the highly abstract hieroglyphics of mathematics that the physicist can speak accurately of the structure of the atom at all.

It is incredible indeed that from within these tiny universes can come the awful energy of an atomic explosion, but it was the fission or "cracking" of a single atom of uranium, the heaviest element, that initiated the conflagration at Hiroshima. Likewise it is from within these infinitesimal reaches that nuclear power is released in controlled amounts to operate the *Nautilus* and other atom-powered submarines. Science thus reiterates the truth that physical size is no measure of strength and potency.

It is possible, in view of these developments, that "mass" as a term of basic theoretical physics may pass out of the picture entirely in favor of its new rival, electric charge. This is a possibility that has been known for some time, but it has not until now received definite experimental support. Thus the inquiries of the early cosmologists for a basic "stuff" to which reality might be ultimately reduced take on a new significance. They were on the right track after all, though it has taken a long time to find it out for certain. At the same time, even if the basic "stuff" of physical reality does turn out to be electricity, as the present evidence strongly indicates, this will not tell us "what" reality is. For electricity itself is a mystery. "Electricity," says Bertrand Russell, "is not a thing, like St. Paul's cathedral; it is a way in which things behave."[8] In fact most modern physicists are positivists who consider it naïve to speak about the "true nature" of anything at all. In most cases they are willing to content themselves with describing the mathematical relationships that exist. In view of the foregoing course of events it is easy to see why. Acquaintance with these facts by those of us who are outside the scientific fraternity should create a new sympathy for the scientist's problems as well as his point of view.

This is the approximate point at which physicists have arrived in their understanding of the fundamental structure of matter. Without doubt there will be further modification of this general view as research continues. But the basic fact has been established, namely, that physical reality is neither metaphysical nor mechanical in nature. The abstract figures of mathematics and the entities with which they deal—electric charge, the speed of light, the convertibility of mass into energy—are more than sufficient to convince us that physical reality is fundamentally dynamic in structure. A physical world in which firmness and substantiality cloak the most radical nothingness (at least as far as is now known), a world in which power and potency seem inversely proportional to physical size, a reality in which the most exciting and determinative events occur in the realm most inaccessible to ordinary experience: This is a strange picture indeed, especially when seen against the background of traditional conceptions. The very first requirement therefore of anyone who would understand physical reality is that he lay aside his common sense notions and empirical prejudices and sit down before the startling facts.[9] "Common sense," says Einstein somewhere, "is merely the deposit of prejudices laid down in the mind before the age of eighteen." We are speaking within strictly defined limits, of course; but even in the area of physical science it is not easy to lay aside our illusions of a solid, substantial reality, of a "building block" universe.

Yet if we regard this situation from a different point of view, we shall find that it need not appear strange after all. Indeed, to the degree that the scientifically informed man of today takes the time and effort to conduct a further inquiry, he is finding that in many ways the transformation from the mechanical simplicities of a century ago into the radical complexities of today is a blessing rather than a curse. And if the theologically trained man will familiarize himself with the foregoing perspective, he may discover striking confirmation of cherished theological convictions. It is to this inquiry that we now turn: What bearing does the scientific understanding of physical reality have upon our Christian understanding of reality?

Chapter II

Dealing with an Obsolete Inference

Certain quite definite implications immediately appear. In the first place, the contemporary scientific view clearly makes obsolete an inference that has long corrupted Christian thought and hampered Christian action. It is the traditional distinction in much Christian thinking between "matter" and "spirit." The distinction between the material and the spiritual is, of course, sound enough, but one of the traditional and popular ways of conceiving it is shown to be obsolete by the scientific information.

For Christian thinking this view originated when the young Christian church came into contact with the life and thought of classical culture. The world out into which the church moved was dominated by the "inert" or "massive" view of reality. Actually, by the time of Christ the original scientific concern of the earlier Greek thinkers had lost most of its thrust. Partly through popular assumption and partly through the influence of the Aristotelian physics, "matter" was identified with the immobile, the objectively physical.

> . . . The Greek world had become increasingly conscious of the gulf between nature and spirit. The tension between the two led in the Hellenistic period to a craving for release *from* nature and *from* the flesh, by all manner of religious disciplines, by meditation, asceticism and sacrament. This outlook impressed itself upon early Christianity in various forms, good and bad, and tended to obscure the biblical wholeness and realism.[1]

In the more exaggerated forms of the classical spirit such as Gnosticism and Neo-Platonism, matter took on a definitely evil connotation, as it did also in Manicheism and in the Oriental mystery cults which flooded the Graeco-Roman world as Classicism lost its inspiration. To be sure, Plato had never maintained that matter or that the senses were by nature evil; he had insisted only that the senses supply opinion and not true knowledge. Therefore, they are not to be trusted in the quest for truth—an insight, by the way, which has been fully vindicated by modern physics. Nevertheless, in the ancient context all these elements combined to contribute to the notion of matter as being a residual mass, having no potential except as acted upon and definitely second-rate in value, if not actually evil in nature.

It is, therefore, not surprising that there developed a bias against what was generally regarded as "the world," roughly identified with "physical reality." Evidences of the false spirituality which resulted are found even in the New Testament. For example, in Colossians 2:8-23 Paul warns his readers not to be deceived by a superficial asceticism but to hold fast to Christ, in whom "the whole fulness of deity dwells bodily." Likewise in Galatians 4:10 he reproaches his readers for observing "days, and months, and seasons, and years."[2]

The influence of these Gnostic tendencies upon the early church was incalculable. For one thing, they were responsible in large part for the church's determination to define its belief, and for this purpose the ecumenical councils were called. The official theology of the church was formulated for the express purpose of combating this false spirituality, probably as much as it was to offset heretical views of Christ. The heart of the creed—"Who for us men, and for our salvation, came down from heaven; And was incarnate by the Holy Ghost of the Virgin Mary"—was a forthright indictment of the view which considered bodily, material reality as something to be shunned or rejected altogether. However, it is unlikely that the creedal statement succeeded in overcoming entirely the false spirituality prevalent in the common mind of the day, and it is not surprising that Christianity became victimized to a definite degree by the cultural situation. Men continued to regard salvation as escape from the shackles of bodily, material reality. Detachment from life was the ideal, not creative, redemptive involvement in it.

This rejection of the world was no doubt strengthened by a generally sordid social situation, by the imperial persecutions, and by the Christian expectation of the early return of Christ. Asceticism and monasticism resulted, along with an exaggerated concern for the salvation of the soul and a corresponding neglect of social and cultural responsibility. It goes without saying that we are not here arguing with history; we are only attempting to show how the conception of physical reality held at the time was markedly instrumental in determining the Church's understanding of its own message, to say nothing of its influence on the world.

This bias against matter and the bodily element was a main tenet of much medieval Christianity. The motif of world rejection was especially strong during Europe's middle period; the Neo-Platonic, introspective approach had a firm grip upon men's thinking about the nature of reality. The Reformation, with its recovery of the genuine New Testament message of the gospel, restored proper emphasis upon the whole life of man, both body and soul. But the effect of this recovery was severely limited because one of the main sources of the bias remained. Nor did Newtonian mechanism change the situation. Matter was still regarded as entirely passive, though now considered to be governed by unchangeable law. The "spiritual" dimension was assumed to be the immaterial, the pietistic; and the ideal of rejection of the world persisted in spite of the insistence of the Reformers that the whole life of man is valuable in God's sight. Thus we find even in Protestant circles the same unfortunate tendency to withdraw from the world, the same inclination to neglect the social imperatives of the Christian message, and—along with these—an exaggerated individualism which has plagued the Protestant movement from its inception. Even in contemporary Protestantism the life of the spirit is all too often shunted off onto a sidetrack, assigned to a special devotional compartment, banished from the market place and the hard realities of life.[3] To be sure, a wrong understanding of physical reality was not the sole cause of these corruptions, but it contributed no small part.

But now science has demonstrated in no uncertain terms that physical reality is fundamentally different from the traditional conception of it. It is neither inert nor rigidly determined by non-physical forces. Rather, it is dynamic in character; whether it is to be regarded as matter or as energy depends purely upon its state at the moment. Far from being always formless and passive, it contains within itself an unbelievable capacity for change and transformation. Indeed, in the modern understanding physical reality takes on some of the characteristics of spirit itself as tradi-tionally conceived. This enriching of the understanding of the physical order strongly suggests that the bias against the material is obsolete and that in today's world we can no longer tolerate the disembodied purism of much traditional Christian thinking.

Happily, this contemporary witness from the physical dimen-sion is paralleled by significant findings of biblical theologians. Study of both the Old and New Testaments has disclosed that man in the Bible is regarded in the wholeness of his person rather than according to the traditional dualism of body and soul. This could be demonstrated in a number of ways, but it will be sufficient to refer to the fully developed thought of Paul as an example. There we find that the true contrast is between *flesh* and spirit rather than between *matter* and spirit. In Paul's think-ing, man "according to the flesh" is man in the solidarity of his earthly existence and, more particularly, man as subject to the powers that control earthly existence—in short, man as he follows the inclinations of his natural state.[4] Man "according to the spirit" on the other hand, is man as he is open to, and as he transmits, the life of God.

The "spirit" of man is thus not to be regarded as a separate part or faculty of man, or even his true nonphysical being as in the customary dualistic way of conceiving it. The "spiritual" man is the new man in Christ, redeemed and free, who lives in the Spirit of God. Oscar Cullmann describes "flesh" and "spirit" in the New Testament as "two *transcendent* powers which can enter into man from without . . ."[5] They are not given with human existence as such. Body and soul—or, more precisely, the inner and the outer man—are originally good in that they are created and given by God. "Flesh" is the power of sin or of death, a power which "seizes the outer and the inner man *together*." On the other hand, "spirit" is the "great power of life, the element of the resurrection," and this power is given through the Holy Spirit. Cullmann goes on to say that the power of the Holy Spirit does not destroy matter, but in "a new act of creation" transforms it, and will in the final resurrection free it from all corruption.

We shall have occasion to return to Cullmann's basic thesis shortly. Suffice it to indicate here the accuracy of this analysis of the biblical view of man. In the New Testament the "spiritual" person is purely and simply—in the totality of his being—the new man in Christ, not the pietistic individual untouched by "worldly" concerns. Spirituality, then, is practically synonymous with "newness." It is the character called forth by the New Age breaking in upon the old order and transforming it into the Order that is to be. Therefore there can be no such thing as a bias against the physical in the name of genuine biblical Christianity. Physical reality is good, because loved into being by a God whose will is the ground of all reality, physical and otherwise. When biblical writers refer to the "world" in opposition to God and his will, they mean simply *the organization of life without God,* not reality in any of its manifestations. Only when it is misused or abused does physical reality become the occasion of evil, and then only because it is perverted by an evil will.

In this context it is practically impossible for salvation and the Christian life to assume a falsely spiritual character. Man in the wholeness of his being is the object of redemption, not the soul only. The body is not the "prison" of the soul but rather the temple of the Holy Spirit, and therein lies the real contrast between the pietistic and the true New Testament teaching. These considerations bear out the point made so strongly by Schweitzer, namely, that the ethic of the salvation of the soul separated from the ethic of the salvation of society in the Kingdom of God is a false separation. How much greater power and influence would the Church have exerted in the world if this wholeness had been achieved and maintained! For one thing, it points up the fact that the distinction between "individual gospel" and "social gospel" is untenable. There is but one gospel, and it is intrinsically related to all the diverse areas of thought and experience, both individual and social.

This obsolete inference regarding the nature of the spiritual has been a main source of much of the contention between science and theology through the years. The traditional conception is still deeply embedded in our thinking, even in sophisticated circles. For example, a recent critic calls in question the tendency by many to see in the change in scientific thinking about physical reality genuine grounds for a spiritual interpretation of the world.[6] This tendency, says the critic, is based on the fallacious assumption that energy is more "spiritual" than are elementary particles of inert matter. The criticism is well made and exposes a serious misunderstanding in the minds of those who perhaps too hastily welcome the new scientific views. Yet the critic himself reveals that he too has an inadequate concept of the spiritual— the same, in fact, as that of those he is criticizing. To be even more specific, both critic and criticized still have in their minds the traditional view we have been attempting to show to be obsolete.

It is indeed not that energy is more "spiritual" than matter merely because it is less "material" than matter. Behind such an idea lies the thought of Plato and Aristotle, not that of the Bible. Both matter and energy are created by God. May we not therefore safely assume that they are of equal value in the sight of God? Spiritual interpretation is a question of status and point of view rather than of intrinsic being. One interprets the universe "spiritually" when he views it with the eyes of Christian faith and when he labors to establish in it the Kingdom which is subject to God. Whether physical reality is matter or energy clearly makes no difference from the ultimate point of view. At the same time, the interchangeability of the two helps to rule out the malignant misunderstanding just referred to and in so doing helps to illuminate the biblical conception.

Much has been done in recent years to bring out the fact that the truly creative element in Christianity is the tension between the present age and the age to come, not between the world of time and a static, timeless eternity. The true contrast, demanding decision on the part of individual and society, is between the old and the new, between the perishing man of self and the newly created man of God, between the man of the "flesh" (in the Pauline sense) and the man united to Christ in the Spirit. Cullmann's metaphor is an accurate one: In the New Testament view the "decisive battle has been fought in Christ . . . only V-day is yet to come."[7] Within this victorious tension of "already fulfilled" and "not yet consummated" the Christian and the Church have their being; and more than this, the entire physical universe shares in it.[8]

The witness from the scientific realm throws light on a related problem upon which there is considerable debate and which has been discussed by Cullmann in the volume referred to above and elsewhere. This is the question of what happens at death. Cullmann insists that the widely accepted idea of the immortality of the soul is "one of the greatest misunderstandings of Christianity."[9] He states that the genuine New Testament view is that the soul is not intrinsically immortal but that it becomes so through the resurrection of Christ and through faith in him. Christians are already living the resurrection life, but this life will not be consummated until the body is also resurrected at the end of history. "The transformation of the body does not take place until the End, when the whole creation will be made new by the Holy Spirit, when there will be no death and no corruption."[10] Those who die in Christ find themselves in a state of "special proximity to God," or as Paul puts it, they are "asleep," they are "with Christ." This interim state is a true interim, however, and the promise of future bodily resurrection at the end of history is contained in Christ's own resurrection. His body is "the first Resurrection Body, the first Spiritual Body."[11]

Allowing for some overstating of his case,[12] it seems that Cullmann's view is genuinely scriptural and that it provides a healthy corrective to modern ideas about immortality. Many an Easter sermon is delivered in praise of man's immortality, dealing with the fact or the possibilities or the intimations of survival beyond death, and really having nothing to do with the New Testament teaching. The New Testament affirms that in Christ the New Age that has broken into this world has established the setting of the heavenly life for those who are Christ's. While they share with others the outward appearances of natural men, they are no longer such, and when they die they are not dead as others are.

It is certain that a great deal of the dynamic of the New Testament is sacrificed when it is forgotten that immortality is a gift of God and not an innate attribute of man. To understand it the biblical way not only heightens the necessity of decision; it also makes for a warm, vibrant relationship to God in Christ. There is nothing more truly emancipating than the realization that fellowship with Christ in love is permanent, that one's own decisive battle has been fought and won, and that nothing—not even death—can "separate us from the love of God in Christ Jesus our Lord" (Romans 8:39b). The heart of Cullmann's argument is impregnable: that Christ could conquer death only by actually and really dying. "When one wishes to overcome someone else, one must enter his territory. Whoever wants to conquer death must die; he must really cease to live—not simply live on as an immortal soul . . ."[13] It is the fact of this accomplished victory upon which the Christian hope is based.

In the light of our scientific information, it begins to appear that the notion of the immortality of an immaterial, nonphysical being—in short, the soul—goes hand in hand with the Aristotelian physics. On the other hand, the New Testament teaching of the resurrection of the whole being of man finds a greater measure of compatibility with contemporary scientific implications. The Bible views human experience as unashamedly physical. Man's whole being, body and soul, is the object of God's saving purpose. At the heart of the older view is the unwillingness or the inability to accept the abiding value of the physical, and it is this which exposes its unbiblical character. The scriptural view, on the other hand, is that in the fulfillment of the divine plan there will be a genuine new creation, not the mere survival of some element of the old. So also the natural world we still apprehend in its outward form is actually in a process of divine transformation.

There is a genuine otherworldliness about Christianity, but it must never be interpreted in an unworldly, falsely spiritual sense. William Temple strikes a healthy note in insisting that Christianity is the most materialistic of all the great world religions precisely because it does regard the material order in such positive terms. The Christian cause is related to all the problems of life and thought, including those involving physical realities—the use of natural resources, the economic and social well-being of man, the aims and the uses of science, and a host of others. Just as the Aristotelian physics is obsolete, so also is any conception of the Christian religion which does not present God and his will as related to the whole life of man.

This parallel between the development of modern scientific views of physical reality and the restating of one of the central doctrines of Scripture, the nature of man in God's purpose, is indeed no modest parallel. It contributes its part to the elimination of hostility and points toward a fruitful relationship between theology and natural science. The change in scientific thinking about physical reality is admittedly no proof of the biblical doctrine, but it is manifestly a valuable witness to it.

Chapter III

. . . And Its Corollary

The antiphysical bias we discussed in the last chapter had even more serious consequences than first appear. Not only were Christian views concerning the nature of man and of the spiritual heavily influenced by current ideas of science, but even the manner in which Christian thinkers conceived God to be related to the world was affected by those ideas. As it turned out, the original inference paralleled and encouraged an unfortunate distinction that gravely handicapped Christian theology for centuries.

Under the influence of the massive, inert view of physical reality, ancient and medieval Christian thinkers developed a "split-level" type of thinking which had far-reaching consequences. God's action in the natural, physical sphere was most often regarded as indirect and by way of "second causes," while his action in salvation and sanctification—that is, the sphere of personal relationship to God—was termed immediate or "supernatural." This distinction was fundamental to the scholastic system of Thomas Aquinas, but it even carried over into Protestant thinking, especially into the orthodox systems of the seventeenth century. The continuation of unsatisfactory conceptions of physical reality made it inevitable that God should be conceived as acting in the physical order only by direct intervention. Everything in reality was understood to occur on the basis of fixed, immutable laws determining the very structure of the physical order.

Physical reality was a "closed" system. The clocklike universe, proceeding on the momentum of its initial beginning, made the agency of God *within* the natural order unnecessary—it could run on and on, so it was thought, without help. By the same token, the intervention of God from *without* the physical order was manifestly impossible—it would only upset the smooth functioning of forces already in operation. To affirm the action of God in the physical order, then, immediately brought Christian thinking into conflict with natural science. Thus it happened that the great problem of Christian theology during the Newtonian era was how God could act at all in a realm governed by mechanism and, if he could, how this action related to his work in salvation. Among other things, the cloistered, individualized Christianity was further encouraged.

In the next section we shall go more deeply into the specific contribution modern science makes to our understanding of the action of God in the physical order. Let it suffice here to say that we behold in the dynamic understanding of physical reality a view that exhibits a basic compatibility with the biblical doctrine of a God who *acts.*

Those familiar with the biblical world will recall that there was little speculative bent in the mind of the Hebrew people. Old Testament conceptions of God and man did not originate in prolonged speculation but in concrete events interpreted according to the prophetic viewpoint. The decisive Old Testament event was the exodus from Egypt; this, the occasion of deliverance from slavery, constituted them into a distinct people, both religiously and nationally. God had *acted* on their behalf, bringing them out with "a mighty hand and an outstretched arm" (Deuteronomy 5:15). To the Old Testament people God was *Yahweh,* who had acted in redemption, and redemption itself was manifestly a dynamic thing. It is generally agreed that it was not until much later that they came to the lofty conviction that Yahweh is also the God of all the earth. The monotheistic faith that Yahweh is the God of history and of creation *followed* the conviction that he is redeemer and savior. This order of things is important, for it is to be expected that Israel should regard the action of God in universal history and in creation to be of the same personal, dynamic character as those deeds they had known in their own history and in personal experience. In other words, we would expect them to conceive God's action in the physical creation to be dynamic also.

Numbers of passages could be cited to show that this actually was the case. Consider, for example, the following familiar psalm:

> Bless the LORD, O my soul!
> O LORD my God, thou art very great!
> Thou art clothed with honor and
>   majesty,
>   who coverest thyself with light as
>   with a garment,
> who hast stretched out the heavens
>   like a tent,
>   who hast laid the beams of thy
>   chambers on the waters,
> who makest the clouds thy chariot,
>   who ridest on the wings of the wind,
> who makest the winds thy messengers,
>   fire and flame thy ministers.
> Thou didst set the earth on its
>   foundations,
>   so that it should never be shaken.
> Thou didst cover it with the deep
>   as with a garment;
>   the waters stood above the mountains.
> At thy rebuke they fled;
>   at the sound of thy thunder they
>   took to flight.
> The mountains rose, the valleys sank
>   down
>   to the place which thou didst appoint
>   for them.
>   . . . . .
> O LORD, how manifold are thy
>   works!
>   In wisdom hast thou made them
>   all;
>   the earth is full of thy creatures

Psalm 104:1-8, 24.

This entire psalm has a clear lyrical quality; but it would be a mistake to limit our appreciation to its subjective aspect. In its vivid dynamism it is movingly descriptive of that Power by whom all things were brought into existence. Such a passage is illustrative of the intense realism of the biblical understanding of God. Surely his action is far more suggestive of modern scientific concepts than of the categories of Aristotle or the mechanism of the seventeenth century!

This testimony to a dynamic presence is found all through the Bible. It is indeed the persistent presupposition of every page. We find it in the opening verses of Genesis where "the Spirit of God was moving" over the yet unformed earth. We see it in the *mysterium tremendum* that Jacob felt at Bethel, the charged holiness that Moses encountered at Sinai, the sublime vision that transformed Isaiah's existence, the light "brighter than the sun" that drove Saul of Tarsus to the ground (see Acts 26:13). There is nothing here of a God who can act in his creation only through second causes or whose action must be interpreted according to a conceptual scheme.

The Hebrew mind was marked by a sense of the immediacy of God's presence in the natural world as well as in personal experience. It was not, then, primitive or childish for the psalmist to address himself to the physical order as if personifying it. This was the case, for example, in Psalm 114 where the Exodus is recalled in a manner that rivals comparison:

> When Israel went forth
> 　from Egypt,
> 　　the house of Jacob from a people
> 　　of strange language,
> Judah became his sanctuary,
> 　Israel his dominion.
>
> The sea looked and fled,
> 　Jordan turned back.
> The mountains skipped like rams,
> 　the hills like lambs.
>
> What ails you, O sea, that you flee?
> 　O Jordan, that you turn back?

> O mountains, that you skip like
>   rams?
> O hills, like lambs?

Then there is the climax, the admonition to

> Tremble, O earth, at the presence
>   of the LORD,
>   at the presence of the God of Jacob . . .
>
>   Psalm 114:1-7.

Such a passage should be sufficient to convince us that the Scriptures know nothing of a God who can express himself in his creation only by intervening in it.[1] The idea of a natural order capable of running along on its own course and by its own power without the continuous sustaining hand of God is utterly foreign to the biblical outlook. The biblical view is that God is *in* his creation, the *whole* of it, including that level studied by the physicist. A dynamic, charged physical reality thus begins to look like that kind of reality which would have been created by the God whose character is disclosed in Scripture.

Further evidence of this the true state of things can be secured by considering directly two widely separated passages. The first is Genesis 3:8 where it is stated that the man and his wife "heard the sound of the LORD God walking in the garden in the cool of the day." This thoroughly delightful verse is not infrequently regarded as of the essence of primitive anthropomorphism, a survival of animistic legend. But to regard it this way is to miss completely its real power and relevance. There is really nothing primitive about it. It is rather a refined, analogical description carefully chosen to convey exactly the meaning of the writer. It expresses in a profoundly dramatic way the holy immediacy of the Father-Creator whose love had been flouted and whose majestic presence now struck fear to the heart rather than joy. In an unforgettable manner the passage conveys the sense of irrevocable guilt and loss with which they anticipated the coming of that familiar Presence whom they had previously known life to life, heart to heart. Such a passage drives home the dramatic, dynamic nature of the biblical doctrine of God; far from being a relic of spiritual adolescence, it illustrates a delicate, mature use of religious symbolism and imagery.[2] Other passages, if carefully studied, will yield the same impression of dynamism and latent power, impressions which grow in stature as we remember what science is saying about the dynamic character of this physical world.

Consider also the 38th and 39th chapters of Job, in which we encounter another striking manifestation of God's action in the physical order. In these chapters God confronts Job with an amazing kaleidoscope of creatures. The biblical reader is prone to see in this confrontation a case of rational anthropomorphism; that is, he takes it to be a demonstration of the wisdom and greatness of God from his works, a demonstration which it is thought will bring a resolution of Job's doubts. Yet it will be seen that this view necessitates the rather comfortable assumption that it is possible for such matters to be demonstrated from nature, an assumption which neither the Scriptures nor Christian theology supports.

Rudolf Otto has put us in his debt by showing that this could not possibly be the real intent of the passage.[3] The creatures depicted actually demonstrate anything but the divine purpose evident in nature. On the contrary, with their mysterious instincts and their inexplicable behavior they show a "complete 'dysteleology,'" a negation of rational ideas of purposiveness. They would be "the most unfortunate examples" one could find of divine wisdom. They show rather

> in masterly fashion the downright stupendousness, the well-nigh daemonic and wholly incomprehensible character of the eternal creative power; how, incalculable and 'wholly other', it mocks at all conceiving but can yet stir the mind to its depths, fascinate and overbrim the heart.[4]

Unfortunately Otto posits a gratuitous "either-or" between the rational and the nonrational, between the familiar and the mysterious, and in our judgment his treatment is weakened thereby. A more adequate view would see the actual merging of the one in the other and the other in the one, and both aspects balanced against each other. We can truly know God in his actions; yet our knowledge is always fraught with the mysterious, the unknowable. It is only the "back" of God that we see, not his "face" (Exodus 33:23). But even allowing for an overstatement of his case, has not Otto supplied a potent biblical illustration of the very kind of divine action suggested by modern physics? The sheer marvel and strangeness, the fascinating mystery of the contemporary scientific understanding of the physical world are amply sufficient to "stir the mind to its depths, fascinate and overbrim the heart." Knowledge does not dispel mystery. Far from it. Knowledge elevates mystery to a new level. It transforms the mere wonder into the wondrous, the bare marvel into a pressing invitation to pilgrimage. And this is what science becomes when we understand its purpose and when we view its findings rightly.

Thus we see that physical reality witnesses to a Power mighty and mysterious, of the same nature as that Power revealed in the Scriptures. While God acts in the physical order in a manner appropriate to that order, there is no question but that his action is of the same dynamic character that we find it to be in the realm of human experience. The reader will recognize that we state this not out of a desire to prove God's existence and nature from his action in the physical order. At the same time, we recognize in these findings of modern science a genuine witness to the truth as we have come to know it in biblical religion.

As a consequence it is necessary to discard the "split-level" manner of conceiving God's agency along with the already-obsolescent idea of a massive, mechanical physical reality. In fact, the very terms "natural-supernatural" are suspect because they imply the perpetuation of an outmoded conception of divine activity. Even "personal-impersonal," the most acceptable substitutes, are not entirely satisfactory because they, too, are misleading. While God acts in a supremely personal way in salvation, his action in the realm of physical reality is not necessarily to be regarded as impersonal. Though the movements of atoms and electrons seem impersonal in themselves, they are still actions of a personal God whose presence is everywhere.

Contemporary existentialism is wrong in thinking that scientific reasoning will of necessity objectify and thus depersonalize man. To be sure, some have allowed science to do this to them, and it is a fact not to be overlooked in defining and carrying out the scientific quest. At the same time, where this has happened it has done so only because science has been misunderstood, cast in obsolete terms of impersonalness. No matter how insistent the existentialist theologians may be that man must be defined only in terms of man, only in terms of personal decision and freedom, thus removing all conceptions of nature and the world, it is extremely doubtful whether this can be done. It is simply not true that the objective world has nothing to do with man's life. Man is man, but he *becomes* a scientist. He perceives truth subjectively, but he also objectifies himself and his world. The scientific task *need* not depersonalize anyone, precisely because it is undertaken in God's world and can legitimately be regarded as a partnership with God in faith. In fact, on this deeper level the partnership between theologian and scientist appears as partnership in and with God. It is the ultimate partnership that establishes the nearer one in its integrity.

The safest course is both the simplest and the most accurate, namely, to be done with "split-level" thinking entirely and to recognize the agency of God wherever dynamic, redemptive events occur. While they will occur most often in the dimension of personal relations, who is to say that God cannot employ physical means to effect his will?

> We are not accustomed to think of the entire life of the universe as mediated from God through Christ in the same sense as our highest spiritual experiences are mediated through him; but that is because we are obsessed with a mechanical view of the universe, and the result is an impoverishment of our thinking. Our physical sciences could not be divorced as they are from our religion if we realized sufficiently that they too deal with a sphere of being in which God manifests himself through Christ . . .[5]

When we view physical reality through the eyes of Christian faith, it is not sunny naiveté that we shall frequently see "books in the running brooks, sermons in stones," and if not "good in every thing," at least in everything the ways in which God will work with us for good.

Part Two

PHYSICAL PROCESSES
BEAR WITNESS

Chapter IV

Physics in a New Key

As one would expect, the transformation in thinking about the nature of the physical world has had profound influence upon natural science itself. Not only has it opened up entirely new areas of reality for natural scientists and technicians to explore and utilize; it has also changed radically the basic terms and concepts in which scientists think of the physical order. Modern physics is pitched in a new key, and the strains and variations of this new theme are being heard wherever men are concerned with truth. We must go more deeply into the implications of the new physics for the theologian and student of Scripture, thus preparing the way more fully for genuine conversation.

No single aspect of the physical order has undergone greater transformation than the understanding of how physical processes occur. Process is a fundamental concept of physics and is, in fact, inseparable from the idea of reality itself. The moment we affirm with modern physicists that the basic fact about physical reality is the interchangeability of matter and energy, the question arises: What is the nature of this interconversion and what are the constituent steps in the process? How do the processes of a dynamic physical reality occur? The best way to grasp the real character of the new era in natural science is to study closely the present state of scientific thinking about physical process. In fact, so vital is the character of physical process that it merits our special and thorough attention.

In a real sense the subject of "how things happen" engaged

the attention of Aristotle more than that of "what things are." Aristotle was impressed with the fact of *motion* and sought to ascertain its causes. It appeared to him that every instance of motion in the world required a *mover,* and that therefore the nature of the process involved could be grasped by determining what caused the motion. His fully developed answer to this question embraced not one but four causes. The *material* cause is "that out of which a thing comes," for example, the bronze of a statue; the *formal* cause is the "form or the archetype"—we would say, the plan; the *efficient* cause is "the primary source of the change," that is, the sculptor; and the *final* cause is "that for the sake of which a thing is done."[1] This fourfold doctrine summarizes both the spirit and the structure of the Aristotelian physics, making causality the very trademark of science as Aristotle viewed it.

When with the advent of modern science the Aristotelian scheme was first challenged and then repudiated, it was the concept of final cause that was singled out for most direct attack. The final cause of a thing was clearly not discernible on either mathematical or experimental grounds, and men of science accurately disdained it as an intrusion of metaphysics into science. But while the attack on final cause constituted the first engagement, in actual fact the whole conception of cause as Aristotle understood it came under fire. As a result of Galileo's experiments in mechanics, motion as the primary consideration in science was discarded and the concept of *force* took its place. With Galileo's formulation of the law of inertia ("A body remains at rest or in uniform straight line motion unless acted upon by an outside force") the Aristotelian physics was definitely overthrown and the foundations laid for the development of Newtonian mechanics.[2] In place of cause according to the philosophical framework of Aristotle came the notion of cause according to natural law. Every process in physical reality was taken to have an ascertainable cause, according to the pattern of the particular law or set of laws applying to the phenomena under consideration.

This was an immensely attractive and successful achievement, as we have already indicated. On the basis of fixed, immutable, universal law scientists erected a "very beautiful and self-consistent theoretical structure."[3] It was also a period of tremendous disadvantage to Christianity, and we shall note more about this shortly. It was not long, however, before it ran into trouble. David Hume struck at the heart of it when he affirmed with convincing experimental proof that the notion of cause is an inferential one, having no necessary foundation in reality itself. Causation, according to Hume, is simply a logical sequence based on previous experience.[4]

Kant's reconstruction of philosophy was contrived precisely because of the need to "save the appearances," i.e., the cause-effect sequence. Kant solved the problem by making cause a category of the mind rather than a category of physical reality itself.[5] According to Kant, the cause-effect idea is valid because the mind makes it so; it does not exist in the process itself but *in the mind which comprehends the process.* Thus in Kant's view the mind of the scientist has an indispensable part to play in the physical process, insofar as it is to be comprehended in scientific terms.

Kant's "Copernican revolution" saved the day for a time, but not for long. The damage had been done. Hume had located the flaw, and not even Kant's admittedly radical solution could prevent the downfall of the mechanistic scheme. Toward the end of the last century the tide began to turn decisively against the rigidity of the classical approach. Repression is the seed of revolution, and the long-repressed sense of selfhood which the mechanistic approach had denied broke through and asserted itself in a new expression of creativity and personal values. Emile Boutroux demonstrated, in a work that has not received the attention it merits,[6] that the ruling principle in physical reality is contingency, not necessity. This was a right-about-face that contrasted sharply with the scientific positivism of Auguste Comte, who was almost a contemporary of Boutroux. The Michelson-Morley experiment in 1887 confirmed the growing suspicion that the Newtonian universe needed revision at certain critical points. Max Planck's development of the quantum theory along with further experimental work on atomic structure in time culminated (once again we are making a long story short) in the principle of indeterminacy of Werner Heisenberg. The indeterminacy principle is thus the outcome of a long period of scientific research on the subject of physical process, and may in a real sense be termed the trademark of modern physics as the concept of cause was the trademark of Aristotle.

In itself the indeterminacy principle simply states that both the speed and the position of an electron cannot be determined at one and the same time. The movements of particular electrons can be dealt with only in statistical fashion; they can be predicted according to the average of all electrons in a definite system in a given time. Instead of working with only one mode or alternative of action—that is, one cause-effect sequence as in classical physics—in atomic phenomena the scientist must deal with many alternatives. All possible modes of action must be considered in the physicist's calculations, because the object *may* respond in any one of those modes. There is a residual unpredictability about the movement of atomic particles that makes a rigid cause-effect relationship absolutely impossible. Only on the basis of a statistical average—like the actuarial tables of an insurance company, which tell *how many* people will die in a certain period but cannot say *which* people—can a definite effect be predicted from a known cause.

The principle of indeterminacy applies centrally in the realm of atomic movements and is the ruling principle on which atomic processes are based. But since atomic processes are manifestly the basis of every physical process regardless of its size or scope, the principle must be understood as applying throughout the whole of physical reality. To be sure, when it is applied to large-scale processes, the indeterminacy is so small as to be practically negligible. At the same time, so universal is the application of this basic principle of uncertainty that the classical system of mechanical process where there is only one alternative involved is recognized to be a "rare and severely limited class."[7]

In fact, if we follow out the implications of this principle, we shall see that no two processes will ever be the same. There will always be differences between them, regardless of the evident similarities. For example, the successive trajectories of bullets fired at a target will never exactly coincide, even though the gun is kept in a fixed position. So many are the factors bearing on the firing of the bullet, its passage through the barrel of the gun, its travel through the air, and its impact on the target that each firing is, strictly speaking, in a class by itself.

To summarize, there is in physical reality no irreducible relationship according to which a given cause must always have a given effect. In a practical sense, of course, the cause and effect sequence will always operate; the wagon moves when pushed and the ball falls when the force of gravity overcomes its upward thrust. But in understanding the fundamental concepts and principles of physical process, the scientist has had to reject the sequence as an empirical, common sense idea that does not really scratch the surface. Cause is a heuristic principle; it is a "way of asking questions, as a child does. . . . [It] allows us to find a path through the confusion of events, in order to know in what direction the investigation 'must proceed so that it shall reach useful results.' "[8]

One significant outcome of this revolutionary development is a new and more flexible concept of scientific law. A law of nature is now regarded as a description of how a given portion of nature customarily behaves rather than a universal mandate determining how it must behave. Physical process includes chance, alternative, probability—and these are definite aspects of the structure of reality, not merely the consequence of inadequate, incomplete understanding. The notion of a law of nature being universally and rigidly binding upon physical reality is no more, as far as authentic physical theory and practice are concerned.

So far, there has been no indication at all of a reversal of these truths, of a reappearance of mechanistic process in physical reality. And this in spite of the earnest hopes on the part of many physicists (including Einstein himself) that reality will again disclose itself to be completely deterministic. "Despite such philosophical convictions . . . the world as it is observed to be in experimental atomic physics continues to behave on a wide front . . . in just the way quantum mechanics expects it to behave."[9]

This brings into view what is undoubtedly the most para-doxical situation in the whole of modern physical science. For the development of the atomic physics of today has demanded an increasing degree of abstraction from familiar, common-sense, easily understandable notions. The more adequate our mathe-matical models, the more profound becomes the gulf separating man himself from the physical world he is studying. The ordinary world of sense perception, the world of experience, must be laid aside while the physicist proceeds by mathematical construction to describe the process under consideration. More and more the human element has been reduced; it may finally be eliminated entirely. There is an impenetrable barrier between sense-reliant man and the phenomena with which the atomic physicist deals. Lincoln Barnett likens the physicist to a blind man trying to discern the shape and texture of a snowflake: "As soon as it touches his fingers or his tongue it dissolves."[10]

In another descriptive analogy Einstein suggests that the physicist is like a man trying to understand the mechanism of a closed watch. "He sees the face and the moving hands, even hears its ticking, but he has no way of opening the case."[11] While the physicist may form a mental picture of the mechanism responsible for what he observes, he can never compare his picture with the actual mechanism itself and can never be sure the picture he has conceived in his mind is the only one that can explain his observations.

There is indeed an irony about this situation in which the scientist's most advanced ideas require the elimination of the scientist himself, even to the extent of being an observer in the process. In fact the scientist as an experimenter more often must simply read the photographically transcribed results of his highly complex experiment rather than observe them directly. There is an inexactitude about the human recording set that makes it notori-ously unfit for achieving the degree of precision science requires.

One's first impression upon encountering this paradox is the feeling that he has lost something. Such concepts of physical science smack of the "smile of the absent cat" made famous by Einstein's reply to just such an objection a few years back.[12] Yet, difficult as it is for the layman in science to believe, what has been gained far outweighs what has been lost.

It is not only that the mathematical models devised by physicists really do work, yielding an ever-closer, more accurate, evaluation of the physical world. In addition to this, in their retreat from mechanistic explanation to mathematical representation, scientists have become increasingly aware of the underlying unity of the natural world. In spite of the difficulty of grasping the mathematical relationships involved, these very mathematical abstractions strongly suggest that there is an underlying level of reality which, while it cannot be reached through the senses, yields itself to expression in mathematical constructions. "It is the mathematical orthodoxy of the universe that enables theorists like Einstein to predict and discover natural laws simply by the solution of equations."[13] But this is simply another instance of the oft-forgotten principle that the higher the flight into the intelligible the deeper the plunge into the real. Therefore to revert to empiricism would be to sacrifice the most advanced knowledge science has gained of how things happen in the physical realm.

But more than this, what has been gained outweighs what has been lost when we think of the relationship between theology and natural science. This we shall attempt to demonstrate in the next few chapters. For the moment let us simply observe how refreshing it is that the game has moved beyond its earlier stages, and to realize that older simplicities which at the time contributed much but which also had the effect of preventing understanding are now gone forever. We must therefore divest our minds of obsolete notions and approach the task in the genuine spirit characterized by the new science. No doubt this will have problems of its own, but at least we may proceed to deal with them without the albatross of older quarrels hanging from our necks.

Chapter V

A Fresh Departure for Thinking

In all likelihood the very first impression one receives as he studies the situation in physical science carefully will be that the changed perspective makes unnecessary much of that deep-seated defensive-mindedness that Christian thinkers have exhibited at times as they confronted the scientific world. Many a Christian has harbored lurking suspicions regarding the real effect that scientific ideas have upon the validity of his faith, particularly as he saw triumph after triumph on the part of the scientist and often chafed under the general impression of irrelevance as he read and heard the pronouncements of some Christian spokesmen. There has already appeared in these pages the theme that theology needs to take serious notice of the information being gathered by the sciences in order that it may remain contemporary and up-to-date. We should pause here to note that the changed situation in science suggests more than a mere reshuffling of the traditional lines between theological and scientific thinking. What it underscores is nothing less than a fresh departure for thinking about the world.

At the very least the new perspective in natural science should make it crystal clear that a comprehensive, systematic interpretation of reality is out of the question. It has been the aim of men of thought almost from time immemorial to achieve a unified, rational philosophy of reality, and some of the greatest names in intellectual history are associated with the undertaking. Plato's conviction was that the deepest reality of a thing is its inner, essential structure, that eternal nature which makes it what it is.

Sense objects, according to Plato, "participate in" eternal ideas and from that participation derive their being; and, conversely, the idea is "represented" in the sense object. Above the whole Plato envisioned an idea of Good which brings specific things into being modeled after the ideas.[1] Aristotle criticized this formulation by saying it is unrealistic to account for the presence of evident realities by having recourse to nonevident realities. Accordingly, Aristotle relocated the idea or form *in* the concrete actuality (*en rebus*). Aristotle's rational structure of things, therefore, is in the shape of an evenly ascending hierarchy from formless matter to matterless form. The place of any particular thing in the whole can be ascertained by determining its final cause.[2]

Centuries later Plotinus assimilated essential insights from his predecessors and formulated an original synthesis which proved to be the last great attempt of classical thought to achieve a comprehensive philosophy of all things. According to Plotinus, the world owes its being to a series of emanations from the One, that which lies beyond all being and thought. All multiplicity, said Plotinus, must rest on an underlying unity, and this unity is the One which is, strictly speaking, unnameable, being the origin of all that is. Ideas are emanations from the intellectual principle, and all living things spring from the soul principle, the energizing cause of movement and life. Since it is an emanation from the divine, the soul is therefore itself divine and can be reclaimed only by laying aside objects of sense and aspiring toward mystical union with its origin.[3]

To a great extent the medieval Christian philosophers took over the same aim and ideal of their classical forebears, but they undertook their formulations from a definite Christian point of view. The great period of Christian philosophy began with Augustine's *nostra philosophia* (although Augustine did not have quite the same systematic goal as his predecessors) and reached its climax with the magnificent sums of knowledge of Thomas Aquinas, Bonaventura, and other thinkers of the high Middle Ages. These great cathedrals of thought paralleled the architectural achievements of the age and are still impressive in their comprehensiveness and detail. They belonged to the cloister and the classroom, however, not to the laboratory, and it is no wonder that with the advent of modern science they were left behind.

René Descartes gave intellectual expression to the modern scientific era when he proposed a new philosophical method, but actually he was simply proposing a fresh orientation for attaining the age-old purpose. Descartes was convinced that there is no limit to what the mind can achieve if it will but follow the methods and principles of geometry. Since geometry deals with plain and incontrovertible truths, Descartes envisioned the same exactitude for philosophy if it will follow the mathematical approach. If he could arrive at a few "clear and distinct ideas" which he could not possibly doubt, Descartes reasoned, then on this basis he could proceed analytically to establish the system of truths accessible to man. In this way Descartes arrived at the fundamental premise, "I think, therefore I am," which he considered to be the clue to existence, since it was the one proposition he could not possibly call in question.[4] Descartes thus bequeathed to modern philosophers their most vexing problem, namely, how the mind which according to him perceives clear and distinct ideas only can have any contact with the outside world at all.[5]

All these attempts to achieve a single, unified, exhaustive rationale of reality were splendid in their own right, but it can be seen now that they were gross oversimplifications of the real problem. The categories in which they were stated were familiar, "common-sense" categories, carefully chosen to satisfy the demands of the mind, not the true proportions of reality itself. This classical philosophical approach was based on the fundamental assumption of a correspondence between the mind and the objective reality it confronts.

Beginning with the modern period this correspondence began to be called in question, and the history of thought since that time has seen the gap between the concept in the mind and the objective world opened ever wider. Now the radical complexity of the physical order confirms the fact that the mind is inherently limited in its aim to formulate such a closed, systematic interpretation of reality. The physical world simply does not correspond in "one-to-one fashion" to man's ideas about it, except insofar as it can be expressed in mathematical terms.

There is mystery in the natural order, a fact upon which Christian thought has long insisted—either directly, or indirectly—through affirming its creation by an infinite, transcendent God. Now, indeed, mystery is freely acknowledged as a constituent element in physical reality, and the limitations of the scientific approach and perspective are frankly conceded.[6]

Nor is this mystery merely "the unknown"; there is much more involved than that. Not only is it the kind of mystery that must be sought out by learned and acute minds; it demands humble and childlike hearts as well. Gilson calls attention to an interesting and revealing contrast seen in the titles of two works published at widely separated intervals.[7] The first, *Christianity Not Mysterious*, by John Toland, was published in 1696 and reflects the general spirit of the Newtonian science as the deists tried to come to terms with it; the other is Sir James Jeans' *The Mysterious Universe*, published in 1937 and embodying the general outlook of modern science upon physical reality after three hundred years of dynamic development and change. Clearly the authentic spirit of science today, as well as its specific findings and teachings, is much nearer the religious dimension than yesterday's conceptions allowed.

This element of mystery can be dramatically observed by considering what science has learned about the nature of light. The transmission of light is one of the most fundamental and universal processes in nature. Yet it is one of nature's supreme mysteries. Certain features of the process can be explained by conceiving it as the passage of waves through space, as for example the emission of electromagnetic waves from a radio broadcasting station. These waves are simply another form of the same radiation as light, and the whole field of radio is dependent upon, indeed, it is established upon, the understanding of light as being essentially wave transmission.

On the other hand, certain other phenomena such as the photoelectric cell demand that light be understood as individual particles or grains transmitted not as a continuous stream but as bundles of energy called photons. All attempts to resolve the resulting paradox or to "crisscross" the two sets of phenomena have met with no success at all. Both interpretations of the nature of the process are necessary to account for things as they are. To the question: Is light a group of waves, or is it particles? the only answer is: It must be both. Thus physical science is in the strange position of having on hand complementary sets of "entirely convincing experimental evidence."[8] Each set has found many practical applications; yet each set, on the face of it at least, logically rules out the other.

This paradoxical situation is now accepted by most scientists as an essential characteristic of reality rather than a temporary contradiction to be eliminated with further investigation.[9] It has been termed the principle of complementarity and is now nearly as well established as its counterpart, the principle of indeterminacy. It underscores in an emphatic way the complexity of even the most common physical processes.

Remarkable as it is in itself, the truly impressive thing about the principle of complementarity is that it furnishes a physical illustration of a troublesome feature of reality that Christian thinkers have encountered many times before. Those who have sought to understand the relationship of God to the world and to the lives of individual men have in most cases been aware that the element of paradox can never be eliminated from this relationship. For example, theologians have long grappled with the paradox involved in holding to both the immanence and the transcendence of God. Certain facets of the Christian experience require the one for their explanation; others demand to be considered on the basis of the other. Prayer, the presence of God in the individual's experience, and the providential care of God are all examples of realities familiar to the Christian that would be impossible and unaccountable apart from the immanence of God; on the other hand, the power of God over all things and his purpose in history demand that he be regarded in the dimension of transcendence. Cyril Richardson puts it in an especially concise and pointed way:

> Here we meet an antinomy, an essential paradox. There is
> no way of overcoming it, and we must leave it at that. . . . That
> is the way God is—absolutely transcendent, single, simple, un-
> veiled, inaccessible, and infinitely above his creation; yet, too,
> he is related to it. He creates, he manifests his love and enters

> into the realm of suffering for our redemption. . . . Everywhere
> we confront the paradox; nowhere can we resolve it. . . . Yet it is
> basic to our faith.[10]

It is not too much to say that the very integrity of Christian theology has been preserved in the measure in which this fundamental paradox has been maintained. Whenever one side of the
matter was emphasized at the expense of the other, some new
heresy was the result. When both aspects of the over-all doctrine
were faithfully adhered to, the biblical teaching and the testimony
of Christian experience itself were sustained. On the whole, Christian thinkers have been commendably "scientific" in determining
to submit to the facts of the biblical revelation and the encounter
with God in Christ, even though they have done so at the cost of
considerable rational difficulty.

Indeed, sufficient instances of this fundamental complementarity of reality are available to convince us that reality is complementary throughout and that the change that has come about in
our thinking about physical reality offers another instance of it.
But it is an exceedingly precious confirmation because by its very
nature physics has been that branch of human thought which has
insisted most emphatically that no such "irrationality" can be finally allowed in the interpretation of the world. Christian theologians who have insisted that the biblical message not be
compromised in the interests of conciliating the demands of a
facile logic should take heart at this confirmation from science of
one of their most precious yet most difficult points.[11]

Here, again, one's first impression may very likely be that he
has lost something, that science has undercut a valuable and hon-
ored ideal of great men of thought through the years. But it is not
so—once again what has been gained outweighs what has been
lost. What the situation demands is not an abandonment of the
attempt to comprehend the world but a fresh departure for that
attempt. In place of the single, all-inclusive method of classical
philosophy, there now emerges the promise of understanding
from dual perspectives. The first of these is the perspective of the
scientific task, characterized by the responsibility to submit to the

facts of nature. Modern science has made short shrift of the requirement that reality must conform to the demands of our logic
before it can be accepted as real. Physics confirms the fundamental observation that the mind is meant to function as a
"knower" and not as a "pseudo-maker."[12]

These two designations describe accurately the two poles between which the human mind has oscillated in its long endeavor
to understand the natural world. On the one hand, there is the responsibility of the mind to submit to the facts of the real world
and to follow wherever these facts might lead in the process of
scientific research and formulation. On the other hand, there is
the malignant tendency of the mind to impose its own interpretations on reality in the interests of achieving systematic intelligibility. The story of the emancipation of modern science is, in a
real sense, the story of the emancipation of the former function
from the shackles of the latter. Only as the mind submits to what
Galileo called "irreducible and stubborn facts" does it reach true
and valid interpretations. It must function as a knower and not as
a pseudo-maker. In following out this requirement of the very
nature of the mind, science has been led increasingly to discard
the kind of familiar notions employed in the classical systems of
philosophy and to make genuine progress to the degree in which
it was hospitable to the facts, however strange they may appear
to be.[13]

At the same time, along with this faithfulness to the facts that
the scientific perspective requires, there is a place for "pure
science," for that speculative theorizing from which have come
some of the greatest achievements in the annals of science. In this
role the scientist is likened to the Sherlock Holmes who, after having gathered the facts and now smoking his pipe or lounging in
his chair, suddenly, by Jove, *has it!* In fact, the starting point in
the physicist's interrogation of reality is "conscious or unconscious
intellectual construction, which proceeds completely free and ar-
bitrarily."[14] The great scientific formulations have been inspired
guesses that worked. But they are "free creations of the human
mind" and not uniquely determined by objective reality itself.[15]
For this reason scientific formulations in themselves can never be

considered final. There may be other formulations that will explain the facts in question, or contemporary formulations may give way to new ones yielding a simpler picture that explains a wider range of physical phenomena. In addition to this, the "inspired guess" or "intellectual construction" must always be expressible in mathematical terms. Again the "mathematical orthodoxy" of the universe appears, and mathematical language is seen to be the indispensable vernacular of physical science.

In its long and laborious development, science has made good its bid for freedom from common-sense notions such as were used by those who formulated comprehensive philosophies of reality. In fact the view of physical reality set forth in these pages is the result of thoroughgoing, disciplined forsaking of empirical, self-evident ideas about physical reality. In its own way science has followed Tertullian's famous axiom, *credo quia absurdum*, "I believe because it is absurd." The development of the modern scientific understanding of reality is an extended commentary on the much-maligned principle of the great African. "What is wrong with science fiction," observes Dr. Edward Teller, "is that it is much too unimaginative." The truth is much more marvelous than fiction—and, more than this, the truth has no deadlier enemy than the common-sense fictions that have been held about it.

In order to function effectively, the scientist must have free rein to explore and investigate whatever facts and features of reality he deems necessary to the successful accomplishment of his task. Religious scruples and sensibilities sometimes lead people to shrink from such inquiries as the scientific study of the Bible, religious experience, and the like. But a moment's thought should be sufficient to convince us that this understandable reluctance is both unnecessary and untenable. Unnecessary because the Bible and other specifically religious realities have validity in their own right and can "hold their own" under even the most exhaustive scientific scrutiny; untenable because for science to yield its greatest benefits there must be no "gap" that can legitimately be declared off limits to scientific investigation. As matters have turned out, the very success of the scientific study of the Bible— to take one example—should be sufficient to convince us of the validity of that study. The limitations of science are the limitations of its *presuppositions*; there is no circumscribed area in which it must stay and out of which it can incur the risk of being charged as "unscientific."[16] The man of science should be welcome in any area of reality, provided of course he comes to his task in the spirit of true science.

The scientist, it is true, should recognize the peril involved simply in being a scientist. This is the peril of what Whitehead terms "misplaced concreteness," that is, accepting as valid and determinative for all of life what one discovers and works with in only a small segment of it.[17] All too easily the scientist becomes what Pascal called "a mathematician who is only a mathematician," one who makes "too deep a study of science,"[18] one who turns a working principle into a universal principle. As much as anyone else—indeed, if not *more* than anyone else—the man of science needs the benefit of an ultimate frame of reference from which the reality he explores can be understood in its wholeness. If this ultimate perspective—which is that of the Bible—is set forth clearly and relevantly, the scientist may be led to discover that it is unnecessary for him to elevate a working principle into a universal principle, to create a "philosophy of science." If he is a man of discernment he will see that many attempts to create such a philosophy are simply reappearances of that age-old hope of the systematic philosophers.

This puts us in a position to see in clear relief the basic difference between scientific and religious language. The purest scientific language is the highly abstract hieroglyphics of mathematics, purged of the empirical, subjective element. On the other hand, the purest religious language is that of dynamic personal relationships, purged of abstraction on the one hand and of a mere subjective individualism on the other. The clearer the mathematical "model," the better science—this will always be true, not only in physics but in all the sciences. The clearer the personal "model," the more genuinely the personal dimension appears, the better theology—this must always be the fundamental base line of relevant, biblically oriented thinking.

If this basic difference is kept in mind and rendered proper respect, there truly need be no "warfare" between science and theology. Not that science can use only mathematical language or theology use only the language of pure personal relationships. This would be manifestly impossible, for neither of the two disciplines could exist under those conditions. The points of contention between them have more often been out in the great middle ground between these two determinative perspectives of the human mind. What we do very definitely mean is that questions must always be referred to the mathematical frame of reference to be decided *as science*; they must always be referred to the personal frame of reference to be decided *as theology*.

Suppose we take as an example the simple inquiry: "What is the nature of reality?" Scientifically speaking, we answer it in terms of dynamic mathematical relationships within the atom; theologically speaking, the question becomes of the order of F.W.H. Myers' great inquiry, "Is the universe friendly?" and must be answered in terms that bear vitally upon man as man. Always the personal model must be kept in the forefront of theological thought. Theology is a formal discipline, but this fact must never obscure its real nature as dynamic engagement. For all its symmetry and comprehensiveness, the *Summa* of Thomas Aquinas stands exposed as a supreme immobilization of Christian truth in a confining prison house of man-originated ideas. And one reason for this is that the personal model has been utterly squeezed out in the interests of formal logic. Accordingly, the fundamental purpose of creed and confession in the Protestant tradition is to formulate and summarize the Christian message in terms which plumb most deeply the personal dimension. For it is in that personal, existential dimension that encounter with God occurs.

We have gone rather deeply into this matter because, as we see it, it constitutes the very charter of a realistic conversation between Christian theology and natural science. And we should say further, it is *partnership* that is needed, not synthesis. One detects in some quarters a growing hope for a "new synthesis," but it is extremely doubtful whether such an ambitious and attractive undertaking is either possible or advisable. It is not only that the radical complexities of the physical order defy systematizing and synthesizing with other truth. Scientific ideas and concepts are too susceptible to change, and the danger of a new scholasticism is all too real. The compromise of the Christian message in a new summation of knowledge that may become obsolete in an all-too-brief time is too grave a risk to take. It is far better that we maintain the two perspectives in their integrity and let each benefit from the contributions of the other.[19]

At the very least, this analysis should bring home the absolute necessity for the Christian thinker to discipline himself in accepting the biblical perspective in its full integrity. Unlike science, theology has no speculative role—and this for the reason that it does not deal in abstract truths at all, but in the dynamic dimensions of personal relationship. As a whole, theology has not made as good in its bid for freedom from common-sense notions as science has; it continues to evidence a tendency to spawn new man-made notions rather than to submit to the facts of revelation recorded in Scripture. The mind has an innate inclination to "gravitate back to the familiar,"[20] and it is precisely by taking refuge in our familiar, comfortable assumptions that we disqualify ourselves from comprehending the true biblical perspective. That perspective, says Paul Minear, is a strange one; it does not agree with our "fund of opinions."[21] It is a unified perspective; that is, no segment of thought contained in it can be understood "detached from its hidden context"; it has in itself a "germinal power and universal relevance that emerges whenever that context is uncovered and appropriated." Furthermore, even the "more objectionable patterns of thought" have an "unsuspected value."[22]

It is this "germinal power and universal relevance" of the biblical message that lay upon us the demand for plumbing that message to its depths, even at the cost of sacrificing our most cherished opinions. The facts of the biblical perspective must be regarded as objectively as those of the scientific if it is to be relevant to a world in which science continues to be the chief molder of thought and action. In addition, it would seem that this faithfulness to the biblical message has a special meaning for Protestantism today in that for one thing it is the real hope of establishing unity within the Protestant ranks. The Protestant movement, centered as it should and must be in the message of God's redeeming grace in Jesus Christ, is radically dependent upon that message in its integrity and vitality. Thus there follows the need for submitting heart and mind to the message so that (as one result) we might be brought into fellowship with one another. "Only as we anchor hope in objective evidence will we be delivered from the sorry business of gaining status by negating each other."[23]

Furthermore, to understand the biblical perspective demands that we receive the biblical message in its entirety. Rudolf Bultmann has proposed that the New Testament be "de-mythologized" in the hope that it can be made more acceptable to those living in a modern scientific age.[24] Certainly his intention is commendable, and some degree of demythologizing is inevitable in biblical exegesis. But if the New Testament is to be made intelligible to the modern mind, it surely must not be done by risking the sacrifice of the New Testament itself. As a matter of fact, it is not by reducing the New Testament to the level of scientific objectivity that we make it relevant to the present, sloughing off those elements that appear to the modern mind to be "mythological" in nature. It is rather by *plumbing as deeply as possible* the biblical history and message and then interpreting that perspective *in its full dimensions* to the modern mind in terms the modern mind can understand. The criterion of correctness must always be how well we apprehend the meaning and purpose of him who speaks to us, not what we might like to hear, to see, or to read. As this is manifestly true in science, it cannot be any less true in theology. "What matters in interpreting the Bible in particular is to apprehend and convey as accurately as possible the thought and intention of the original writer in his own situation."[25] For this we need every element, every word of the record. At the same time, this is not to suggest a new bibliolatry; it is to facilitate that very process of cultural translation for which Bultmann correctly sees so demanding a need.

In fact, if we study the matter more closely, we shall see that the real problem in understanding the Bible is not the thought world and cultural context in which its message is embedded and which are apparently so strange to the scientific mind. It is rather the ideas and opinions we often import *into* the Bible in the very process of trying to interpret it. After all, the very essence of the scientific spirit is to recognize the facts, even though they may appear strange enough. The true man of science will not be frightened away from the Bible by, for example, the miraculous dimension reported in it. He will investigate it, to be sure, bringing to it every tool of study he has in order to determine precisely what it means, drawing on the knowledge of others, appraising it from every angle of vision to arrive at a clear conception of its importance for the message of the Book as a whole.

Further, he will then appraise his own received ideas in the light of the fresh information received, the difference it may make, and the fuller understanding it may bring. Then he will make his decision accordingly. If he is a true man of science, he certainly cannot do less than this. Least of all can he allow his search for the truth to be jeopardized by his own preconceived, subjective ideas of what the truth will turn out to be, even if these ideas seem for the present to enjoy the designation of being "scientific." "What are the facts?" he must ask. And the facts must then be given opportunity to vindicate their own importance. Thus the student of Scripture, whether he is a scientist or not, will find repeated for himself that experience of Augustine, who through his lifelong study of the Bible found his ideas becoming more and more truly scriptural, until at the end of his days he could sit in judgment on his earlier writings and wish they had been more Christian.

When one disciplines himself in thought and life to discern and receive the genuine biblical message, he will discover the more glorious counterpart of what as a scientist he finds in his investigation of the natural world. As a student of nature he encounters the strangeness of the reality he studies. As a student of Scripture he discovers the strangeness of the ways of God revealed in his dealings with ancient Israel and in Jesus Christ. He will have brought home to him the fact that there is indeed a "strange new world within the Bible." But it will be one that strikes a responsive chord and that warms his heart by its strangeness rather than one that drives him away—just as the view modern science gives fascinates and awes him as he ponders it at length.

To be sure, as a student of Scripture he will not become so engrossed in the world of the Bible that he loses contact with and appreciation for his own world of time and nature; nor will he as a student of nature allow himself to forsake the living God, the ultimate Reference who gives meaning and sanity. On the contrary, he will come to see how truly inseparable the two are, this remarkable world of creation and the equally remarkable world of revelation. Furthermore, as he moves deeper into them, coming in "the unity of the faith, and . . . the knowledge of the Son of God, unto a perfect man, unto the measure of the stature of the fulness of Christ" (Ephesians 4:13, KJV), the student will experience in ever-fuller measure the mystery of God and his world and the even more awesome mystery that we are his.

Chapter VI

A New Open-mindedness

The unexpected but unchallenged enlargement of man's thinking regarding one of the fundamental concepts of science, that of physical process, will of necessity have far-reaching implications not only for science but for all areas of thought and life, including the theological dimension. Indeed, it is this one factor which has done most to bring about the better climate of understanding between the world of scientific and the world of religious thought. Through the years the scientific understanding of how physical processes occur has had profound influence upon theological ideas, whether the science was of Aristotelian or Newtonian or some other inspiration. It will be our purpose in this chapter and in the next to follow out two of the theological implications of the change from mechanistic ideas of process to those of quantum physics. There are other implications, no doubt, but these two at least are of basic importance for theology generally. One such change which has important consequences is that from regarding reality as a "closed" to an "open" system.

We have already noted how the triumphant days of Newtonian physics were days of decided disadvantage to Christianity. In the face of the seemingly insurmountable task of having to develop an adequate conception of God's action in a world conceived to be governed by immutable scientific law, some Christian spokesmen endeavored to make Christian truth compatible with the prevailing scientific and philosophical climate. They set forth the Christian faith as being "as old as creation," the "republication of natural reason," thereby sacrificing a vital, vibrant theism to a bare and sterile deism. Thus revelation, miracle, and the purposeful action of God in history were ruled out from the beginning.

The efforts of the deists appear to us all the more ironic because at their base lies the erroneous mechanism of Newtonian physics. Since in the light of modern developments no such deterministic clockwork can be found, it can be said that the contemporary view gives positive scientific grounds for considering physical reality to be "open" to the presence and agency of God. The alternatives and probabilities leave room for the operation of a purpose not observable at the intellectual level alone. This change of outlook cannot, it is true, be legitimately invoked in the demand that we acknowledge the agency of God in the natural order. But it does mean that a new open-mindedness is in order, and that a Christian view of reality becomes tenable even on scientific grounds.

The subject of a world view has been of more than passing interest in the revival of Protestant theology in this century, though more in a negative than in a positive way. Karl Barth has been insistent that the theologian must disclaim any interest in, or responsibility for, a world view.[1] Barth identifies a world view with a philosophical interpretation of reality which leaves out the agency of God, and since he obviously can have nothing to do with the latter, he must of necessity rule out the former. This rejection of a world view has been characteristic of the Barthian approach and is part and parcel of his reaction against the watered-down Christianity of nineteenth-century liberalism. But we must insist that Barth's rejection stems from his reaction, not from the positive proportions of the Christian faith.

Let us examine the subject of world view more closely. The dominant feature of any world view is a faith-principle comprehensive enough to give meaning to human experience and compelling enough to demand conscious and willing obedience. The organizing principle of the liberal world view, for example, was the ethical understanding of the Kingdom of God. Events have demonstrated the inadequacy of this purely ethical concept, but they have not demonstrated the inadequacy of a world view as such.

Actually there are numerous world views, as many in fact as

the faith-principles—the "dominant ideas"—men use to interpret and organize experience. Such principles and ideas are fundamental to any intelligible comprehension of reality, whether it be according to a specifically Christian orientation or not. The trouble arises in the fact that whenever such a rational concept is made the basis for a world view, it inevitably oversimplifies the actual situation which the observer confronts, leaving out vital facets of authentic experience or interpreting them according to insufficient presuppositions. Worse than this, the active agency of God is often sacrificed to a rationalistic scheme which purports to be able to explain and account for everything that goes on in reality. In this manner a world view becomes an ideology, and a new "ism" appears on the scene.

Surely, however, the way to meet the situation is not to reject a world view outright as being of little importance, but rather to formulate in terms relevant to the modern scene the authentic Christian view of reality. Experience has shown that to abandon the field does not solve the problem. It only opens the door to a host of new "isms" and half-gods that usher in new enslavements of the mind of man. The encouraging factor in the situation today is that the changed perspective regarding physical process makes it possible to hold to an authentically Christian understanding of reality, and to do so in terms which are not unfriendly to science.

Much of the suspicion directed against a world view from within Christian circles stems from the mistaken belief that there is such a thing as a scientific world view, and that this latter forms something of an "ace-in-the-hole" of those who espouse rational world views of various inspiration. Here is another, less obvious, manifestation of the "conflict" between theology and natural science, but an indication nonetheless of the harm caused by misinformation and misunderstanding on both sides. Believing that there is a scientific world view which is thoroughly scientific, Christian spokesmen have shied away from joining battle with such a formidable foe. They have sought other ways of interpreting the Christian religion, ways which would continue to assure the integrity of the Christian point of view in a scientific climate but which would avoid outright dispute on the point of basic understanding. Thus the gap between theology and natural science has been perpetuated or even widened. Valuable as it is, the existentialist approach is motivated in part by this unconscious—or conscious—fear of being shown to be "unscientific" in one's religious beliefs.

As long as Newtonian mechanism was the organizing principle of science, then there could be said to be in truth a scientific world view. Reality was a closed shop and it was vain to speak of a *rapprochement* on truly Christian terms. But the downfall of the mechanistic principle calls in serious question the existence of such a thing as a scientific world view. It betrays the revealing fact that what often goes under that name is not really "scientific" at all; it is rather an agnostic world view using the data of science. Its credibility is due to the supposed agnostic or even atheistic character of science—truly a gratuitous assumption on any count. Science as now understood does not offer any such principle firmly enough grounded in physical reality itself to serve as the basis for such a rationalistic world view. Neither indeterminacy, nor quanta, nor complementarity, nor relativity can stand as the basis for a satisfactory and comprehensive world view. The difficulty stems from the fact that they are vulnerable and can be pressed into service by those intent on demonstrating an agnostic understanding of reality.

Every generalization made in natural science is in a real sense a precarious victory over the radical complexity of the facts. "Scientific positivism" does not come from within science itself but from the positivistic presuppositions men bring with them into the study and interpretation of science. It appears, then, that what we are dealing with in the contemporary situation is not an inherent and necessary hostility between a scientific world view and a possible Christian world view, but rather a theological exclusivism based in large part upon an obsolete understanding of physical process.

Helpful light is shed on this point in a recent historical study of the relation between the findings of geology in the decades before Charles Darwin and convictions generally held at the time by Christians regarding the Genesis account of creation.[2] C. C. Gillispie suggests that the substitution of the term "science" for the earlier term "natural philosophy" near the end of the eighteenth century made it more difficult to associate scientific insights with religious insights. "Natural philosophy" has a "humane and comprehensive sound," while "science" connotes, for the layman at least, something "technical, abstruse, and even a little forbidding."[3] To put it plainly, men found it harder to attach providential implications to the idea of science than to that of natural philosophy.

It may be that part of the complication of this present situation is the fact that it involves a basic prejudice of the mind as much as it does an obsolescent impression of hostility, although the question of attitude is too indefinite and imprecise to bring into clear focus. But whether this is true or not, the contemporary scientific picture leaves no room for such a prejudice. As matters have turned out, the discarding of the term "natural philosophy" has been a definite gain, though it may have meant the temporary discrediting of the providential point of view. As a matter of fact, the "providential point of view" was sometimes more of a hindrance than a help, inasmuch as the real problem at the time, says Gillispie, was not so much religion *versus* science as it was religion *in* science.[4] Natural philosophers introduced a providential faith-principle into geology in the attempt to arrive at a world view compatible with both science and their theological convictions. But the effect of this was to hinder both the development of science and the needed clarification of the Genesis creation account. Now we may say that as the "providential point of view," as a faith-principle imported into science, and the determinism of Newtonian physics both fade into the past, the genuine biblical understanding of reality comes into view.

"In the beginning, God"—this is the indispensable charter of a Christian understanding of reality. It is not so much a rational principle as it is an *event* calling forth an act of creative acceptance.[5] It is, to be exact, the only affirmation man is able to make that supplies wholeness and ultimate meaning to man's life. It is the only basis (within the over-all biblical context, of course) upon which all facets of human experience and human history can be adequately understood and appropriated. And this includes the rational dimension. That this is God's world and that he is at work in it, creating, sustaining, redeeming—this we must receive as the indispensable "given" for a meaningful approach to reality. A Christian world view does not necessitate a synthesis of biblical truth and scientific or cultural fact in the manner of the natural philosophers to whom Gillispie refers. It is the *perspective* that is the chief thing, not the rational principle as such. The "Christian approach to reality" is perhaps a better designation of it than "Christian world view," since the latter appears to refer only to the rational dimension.

The Christian approach to reality is far more comprehensive than the rational, pure and simple. It includes a way of life as well as a way of thought. It necessitates commitment as well as comprehension, action as well as interpretation. In fact, real comprehension is impossible without commitment; it is those whose "will is to do his will" who come to know in their own experience the truth of the Christian teaching.[6] The important thing about Christian philosophy—as we pointed out in the last chapter—is that it be understood and undertaken as the interpretation of reality from the perspective and the experience of faith in God as Creator and Redeemer. It should not be the formulation of another system of philosophy on the basis of a biblical faith-principle. Unfortunately this is what Roman Catholic thinkers have made it, following the inspiration of Thomas Aquinas. Perhaps it is at this point that Reformed theologians need to give their supreme effort; for it is the Reformed tradition that best embodies and preserves the perspective we are discussing.[7]

God is working his purpose out, not according to some rationally observable plan but in the alternatives and contingencies of all of life, in a way that calls us repeatedly to commitment and service. Not only does the contemporary scientific situation permit such a point of view, but it even supplies a "clue" by which the action of God can begin to be understood. We shall deal with this "clue" in the next chapter. For the moment let it suffice to note that the "openness" of the physical order is an open door inviting us to a Christian approach to reality, to an ultimate vantagepoint that gives wholeness and that brings sense and purpose into every aspect of man's life and experience.

We find additional confirmation of the importance for Christian thought of the changed views of physical process when we study carefully the nature of scientific investigation and experiment. Science is not, as the uninitiated might conceive it, a plodding drudgery by which the bare facts of an uninteresting nature are observed and catalogued. On the contrary, if reality is "open" to the agency of God, then it follows that there is more to the discipline of scientific research than the mere accumulation of facts. The work of the scientist frequently takes on the character of *encounter*. The scientist has found that nature has the strange—but not so strange—capacity to respond; he not only searches for the truth, he often finds that the truth "comes to meet" him, as it were.

No doubt the best procedure here is to let the testimonies of some men of science speak for themselves. The experience of Sir Malcolm Sadler seems representative of that of many scientists. Says Sadler:

> The ideas come to me unsought and I find them in my mind exactly as I might find a half-crown that someone had put into my pocket while my coat was hanging up in my absence.[8]

Chance plays an important part in all true scientific research. Some of the most important medical advances have stemmed from chance discoveries in the laboratory. Yet Louis Pasteur once remarked, "Chance visits only the prepared mind." This insight, by the way, expresses well the unique combination of intuitive search and natural response that constitutes true research. The late N. R. Campbell relates an experience typical of many who work intensively on a specific project or program of study. He describes how a copy of a philosophical magazine fell out of his bookcase and lay open on the floor:

> Some algebraic formulae caught my eye . . . it was part of a paper by a Mr. N. Bohr, of whom I had never heard. . . . I sat down and began to read. In half an hour I was in a state of ex-

citement and ecstasy, such as I have never experienced before or since in my scientific career. I had just finished a year's work revising a book on Modern Electrical Theory. These few pages made everything I had written entirely obsolete. That was a little annoying, no doubt. But the annoyance was nothing to the thrill of a new revelation . . . And I had so nearly missed the joy of discovering this work for myself, and rushing up to the laboratory to be the first to tell everyone else about it . . . twenty years have not damped my enthusiasm.[9]

It is easy to see that there is in such a creative moment more even than the mere joy and thrill of a new discovery. These moments—comparatively rare, admittedly, but undoubtedly real—come with the authority of a disclosure that grips and humbles. "Before these mysteries of life," exclaimed Jean Henri Fabre, the entomologist, after he had studied the process of cross-pollination of flowers by insects, "reason bows and abandons itself to adoration of the Author of these miracles."[10]

Such sentiments are clearly religious and they cannot be attributed merely to the rapture of the moment. They reflect the attitude of many profound scientific minds, including that of the foremost man of science of the age. Albert Einstein was a deeply religious man, though not associated actively with any religious institution. The following often-quoted paragraph summarizes his convictions regarding religious awareness:

> The most beautiful and profound emotion we can experience is the sensation of the mystical. It is the sower of all true science. He to whom this emotion is a stranger, who can no longer wonder and stand rapt in awe, is as good as dead. To know that what is impenetrable to us really exists, manifesting itself as the highest wisdom and the most radiant beauty which our dull faculties can comprehend only in their most primitive forms—this knowledge, this feeling is at the center of true religiousness.[11]

This "sensation of the mystical" is quite unstructured and partially emotional, to be sure, and is no doubt encouraged by unconscious religious presuppositions already in the mind. It is certainly not substantial enough to build upon in the hope of producing a natural theology after the example of the medieval theologians.

Indeed, all attempts to construct a natural theology necessitate the superimposing of an ideological form upon the facts of nature and in effect issue in a new—albeit religious—scientism. This procedure is quite unscientific as well as being unsupported by the biblical revelation. Yet it would be equally unscientific—and also unbiblical—to fail to acknowledge the revelatory element in true science.

At this point one of the basic affinities of the Reformed tradition of Christianity with the tradition of modern science appears in clear relief. The Reformed point of view in theology made express provision for a notion of "general revelation" along with the historical revelation recorded in the Scriptures.[12] What is emerging here in the experiences of experimental scientists is a confirmation of this doctrine. There is a witness additional to and wider than that in the Bible. Muted and insufficient it may be, but even Scripture itself suggests it.[13]

It is unfortunate that Reformed theologians have not allowed this aspect of their theological heritage to spur them to a more diligent study of God from his works, and as a consequence a vital element in Christian truth has been neglected. The sovereignty of God is a creative, dynamic doctrine, the full meaning of which no one has yet exhausted. In the days following the Reformation the original wholeness it was intended to convey was lost in the concern to consolidate and to systematize the known theological gains that had come with the Reformation. Perhaps this was inevitable since Newtonian mechanism appeared to bar the way to a truly creative approach to reality in its wholeness. But if we take seriously both the theological and the scientific perspectives of this present hour, then it becomes clear that the days of such narrow orthodox exclusivism are numbered. The developing partnership between men of religious faith and men of science may lead Reformed Christianity to a recovery of a vitally important factor of their theological heritage. If so, it can have a meaning beyond what we are now able to see.

Attention is being given in some circles to the development of just this wider view of revelation, a view which is reminiscent of the early Reformed insistence.[14] It is undoubtedly one of the most important areas of theological discussion today, especially in view of the continuing controversy over biblical authority. More than this, it is important for the development of a truly Christian view of reality.

Much depends upon the attitude which the Church takes regarding this matter. If it proudly refuses to acknowledge the possibility of any revelation other than that given in the Scriptures, it will rightly incur the displeasure of scientists and probably fail to profit by what science is saying about the universe. On the other hand, if the Church were to take the data of science and pour it into a ready-made *philosophia perennis* adequate for all things divine and human, it must not be surprised if the scientist turns away disappointed. The Church has a responsibility to its own men of science who are heroically maintaining the Christian point of view in science against the growing secular-mindedness of the times. In addition, it must increasingly be able to approach the scientist of secular mind in a spirit of appreciation and with the promise of a higher point of view which gives true wholeness and meaning. We cannot do this with a closed mind. We must approach the scientist and the scientific mind generally not only as witnesses to the supreme Reality revealed in Jesus Christ but also as learners of a lower medium through which that same Reality discloses himself.

It must be insisted that the recognition of this wider view of revelation does not in any sense lessen the importance or the authority of the biblical revelation. On the contrary, it strengthens the position of the Bible as the record of God's unique revelation of himself in the history of the Old Testament people and supremely in Jesus Christ. Revelation on the level of physical reality is no more than a vague intuition of divinity, of mystery, of a "something more." The "curious order" that underlies scientific judgments is profoundly suggestive, but there is "too little to affirm"—although "too much to deny."[15] Not all men of science testify to the type of experience on the scientific level we have been discussing; one has "eyes to see" and "ears to hear," while another does not. Some are aware of a sense of mystery or transcendence but do not ascribe to it any religious associations. But it is a matter of *human response* rather than ability or inability on God's part.

Reality is sacramental, as William Temple maintained in his famous Gifford Lectures.[16] God discloses himself through every level of reality according to the mode of existence of each level. Indeed, this must be true if any revelation at all is to be possible: "We affirm, then, that unless all existence is a medium of Revelation, no particular Revelation is possible."[17] That which can be inferred about the transcendent dimension on the level of physical science thus calls out for fuller light. Only to the eyes of faith— biblically renewed and informed—can the Creator be seen in the creation.

What was known about reality before the advent of modern science was never so marvelous and majestic as we now know it to be. Yet all the discoveries of science have not depreciated the knowledge of God disclosed in Scripture one whit. Indeed, the opposite is true. As knowledge of the universe expands and man's position within it becomes both more central and more critical, so increases the demand for meaning, as well as for effective means of moral and spiritual control of the achievements science has made possible. Science cannot give these. The scientific task fosters integrity and character. A persistent and passionate devotion to truth cannot help but build trustworthiness in the man who engages in that quest. But science is not at all sufficient to itself. It is, after all, quite limited as far as being able to answer the real questions is concerned. The "philosophy of science" is in itself a radically truncated study, and especially so in a world of relativity and quanta. Never was the biblical message of God's redeeming grace in Jesus Christ more relevant to the human situation than today. Never was it more imperative that we accept and that we represent the Christian view of reality, at the very heart of which is the purposeful, redemptive action of the sovereign Creator of all things and Father of all men. This is still the birthright of Christians and especially of Reformed Christians—yes, even in this world of modern science.

Chapter VII

Chance and the Purpose of God

The dynamic view of physical reality which modern science discloses has been impressed on us as a view compatible with the action of the Creator as revealed in Scripture. The revision of understanding regarding physical process has resulted in a more flexible conception of scientific law and thereby permits more freedom in formulating the Christian view of reality and of the way events happen. The central question of our study now appears: Is it possible to regard the same event or series of events simultaneously from both the scientific point of view and the theological point of view? And, if so, how?

As we saw earlier, this is at the very heart of a satisfactory relationship between theology and natural science. It is one thing to state that theology and natural science present views which are basically compatible with each other. But if we are to move in the direction of genuine wholeness, then we must be able to regard one and the same event from both the theological and the scientific viewpoints and have each of these perspectives remain sound in itself. In short, we must know whether one may be both a theologian and a scientist at the same time, and if so, how—how one may feel that he is not compromising his principles as a theologian while he is engaged in the tasks of natural science and that he is not being "unscientific" when he turns his attention to theology.

This part of the subject has been treated so effectively by one of our leading scientists that it is best at this point to summarize and then apply further the essential features of his argument. W. G. Pollard, Director of the Oak Ridge Institute of Nuclear

Studies, has made one of the most important contributions to the modern conversation between theology and science.[1] He calls attention to a common misunderstanding according to which chance is regarded as being in itself a causal agent. It is often said of an event that "it was due to chance" as though chance were the reason behind it. As a matter of fact, it is quite common parlance to regard events as often happening "by chance" without real attention being given to the nature of chance. In his book, *Human Destiny*, Lecomte du Nouy treats chance as a causal agent. He attempts to demonstrate that the evolutionary process could not have occurred "by chance" and that therefore God's "active providence in evolutionary process is . . . essential to an understanding of it."[2]

Pollard insists, however, that chance in itself cannot be the cause of anything. "The attribution of chance to events is just the opposite of the assertion of their cause."[3] If chance itself were a cause, then there would be no room for those alternative courses of action which the contemporary understanding of physical process includes. The occurrence of chance in the natural order, Pollard insists, does not rule out the agency of God as if "chance" were able to account for the event wholly of itself. On the contrary, it is precisely the factor that makes it possible. Chance enables us to regard one and the same event as "under the full sway of all laws of nature and natural causality and at the same time under the full sway of the divine will."[4] What is seen as chance in the laboratory and from the scientific perspective can without contradiction be regarded as the will of God in history and from the perspective of biblical faith.

> Science deals with a single happening only in terms of the way it falls into the pattern of repeatable events which can happen in a given set of circumstances. Providence, however, ignores all else which might have happened but didn't, and focuses its attention on the one thing which did happen in a given setting in history.[5]

Chance and providence are thus not mutually exclusive of each other; indeed, they must be regarded as mutually dependent if either is to be understood fully.

This clarification of the nature and the limitations of the concept of chance removes one of the most formidable barriers to a genuine good-neighbor policy between science and theology. As a consequence we can affirm that physical reality is not only "open" to the action of God, thus making it possible to formulate the Christian view of reality, as we have shown in the preceding chapter. Events can also be interpreted simultaneously from both the scientific and the theological points of view. Providence is not in every case to be thought of as the introduction of a new force which changes the course of nature without observable cause. It may be understood as the ordinary pattern of things working out just as science observes it but now seen from the fundamentally different point of view of faith in God.

A practical illustration will help at this point. According to statistical scientific law, for every 100,000 persons vaccinated for smallpox one such person will actually contract the disease. This is a statistical average arrived at through computations derived from the large number of persons vaccinated. The fact that my child did not take smallpox when he was vaccinated may be considered on my part as a special providence of God, especially if it appeared for a time that he had. Nor did the scientific context of the situation make prayer of no effect, since it could not be ascertained on scientific grounds which person of the 100,000 vaccinated would take smallpox. From the standpoint of statistical law, I must acknowledge that it could have very well been my child, even though the odds seemed heavily against it, but from the providential point of view—which deals only with the way things actually did happen—I bow my head in grateful worship. If the situation had turned out the other way, the response called forth from me would certainly have been different—for such a case of smallpox is nearly always fatal. But the scientific complex of the event need not have prevented me from regarding even *that* as providential, provided of course my faith was strong enough to accept it as such.

Providence may be defined as the divine employment of chance for the furtherance of God's purpose of redemption. *That* an event subject to chance and probability occurred is clearly a subject for scientific study, as is also the fact that it may happen again. But what appears as chance to the human observer is not therefore beyond the operation of one whose "thoughts are not our thoughts and whose ways not our ways." *Why* the event should have occurred just when and where and with the effect it did is a matter calling forth response from one who believes in the providential rule of God. R. W. Stewart sums it up in an illuminating paragraph:

> Purpose, indeed, far from being incompatible with chance, presupposes the reality of chance; only if events are haphazard can there occur that arbitrary interference and interaction with the stream of casual occurrences which constitutes purpose. Purpose is essentially the will to impose some order or aim upon chaos. It is realized only in action, and it takes one whose own will is in some way involved to discern purpose. . . .
>
> If exactly fitting parts come along the conveyor belt, no room is left for purpose in putting them together. The operator's task is purely mechanical. But because casual imperfections and variations may and do occur, and demand a certain amount of fitting or adjustment, there is a measure of scope for purpose in the worker. It is the element of chance that makes purpose possible.[6]

The Bible itself offers the best illustrations of this dynamic view of providence. Familiar to every Sunday School child, the story of Joseph is regarded by many as the classic example of the providential purpose of God being fulfilled through a pattern of chance occurrences. A father's favoritism, a young boy's dream, the jealousy of brothers, a passing band of nomads, a woman's frustration, a butler's forgetfulness, an economic situation demanding foresight as well as insight, a famine in the homeland —from the human point of view these appear to be factors entirely accountable in terms of chance occurrence and human motivation. Probably not even Joseph himself was able to regard them as anything more than occasions or situations in which he simply determined to "make the best" of existing circumstances. Certainly neither he nor anyone else could have predicted the outcome. Only when the entire story had reached its completion, could he—looking back over the amazing course of events—say to his brothers, "You meant evil against me; but God meant it for good" (Genesis 50:20). Even then, it was the operation of a master purpose *within the pattern of events themselves* that constituted the providential nature of the whole process. It is obvious that this purpose did not in any way preclude the exercise of human will at every point.

Equally as striking an instance of this purposeful employment of chance events appears in the later chapters of the book of Acts. Paul, having determined to go to Rome, feels constrained to return to Jerusalem first with the offering for the relief of the needy Christians in the holy city. Little could he have realized that in setting out for Palestine he was actually launching on a course that would bring him eventually to the destination he really desired to reach. Through arrest, riot, prison, witness before governors and kings, through storm, shipwreck at sea, and the unexpected hospitality of natives, Paul's path led to Rome. There is drama of the highest order in the simple yet moving text, "And so we came to Rome" (Acts 28:14b). From the human point of view Paul's experience appeared as a series of loosely related events easily attributable to chance: a Jewish friend mistaken for a Gentile, a timely revealing of his Roman citizenship, the thwarting of a murder plot by the chance presence of his nephew who overheard and reported it in time, the appeal made to Caesar in order to escape certain death in Jerusalem, a captain's miscalculation, contrary winds, the storm at sea, and the appearance of a certain "bay with a beach." Every one of these events can be "explained" in terms of natural circumstances and human decision. Probabilities and alternatives were legion at practically every point. But from the standpoint of the providential purpose, each random event played its part, each decision freely made on the human level contributed to the advancement of the master plot, though not by any means in the way a human agent would have planned it.

In the mystery of the purpose of God human freedom and effort are saved from frustration and futility. The affirmation of providence does not at all mean the denial of human freedom; on the contrary, providence is the employment of freedom to accomplish divine ends. On the other hand, the purpose of God must never be regarded as a blueprint. Seldom, if ever, can his actions be anticipated. God is "the great Doer of the unexpected" and the Scriptures "a record contrary to expectation."[7] The Bible testifies on nearly every page to instances of God's action which would have been wholly unpredictable from the human point of view, so that we can say in truth that his ways are "unsearchable" and his judgments "past finding out." The so-called "scandal of particularity" by which the God of the whole earth chooses particular men and nations to effect his purposes takes its place within this wholly unpredictable course of things. Even so, the divine intervention and call never occur apart from the element of faith in the hearers. In every instance, the important factor is not the particular overt manifestation of God's choice, but the eyes of faith that recognize the action of God in the events that have happened. Thus through all the matrix of events and circumstances that may on the human level help determine the situation, the Scriptures testify to an infinite steadiness of purpose according to which God's design is being accomplished in history and human experience.

At this point a fresh perspective emerges on the perennial problem of miracle. The modern mind is prone to regard miracle as a violation of the laws of nature and therefore almost by definition untenable. However, the reinterpretation of natural law to which we called attention in the preceding chapter discloses in itself the basic error of such a view. It shows that the mutual exclusiveness of the theological and the scientific domains—the exclusiveness which has dominated the scene for so long and which is in great measure the real source of the "problem" of miracle—is obsolete and unsound. If physical reality is open to the agency of God, then miracle is not as unscientific and unnatural as it appears to be. At the same time, the contemporary views of science enable us to regard miracle from a somewhat different point of view than traditionally understood.

Many biblical miracles do not involve the question of a violation of a law of science at all. Their miraculous character springs from their extreme improbability rather than from the setting aside of a normally operative scientific law. Pollard regards the Israelites' crossing of the Red Sea as a supreme illustration of such a miracle.[8] Embedded in the account as given in Exodus 14 and 15 we find the essentials of this epochal event: the flight from Egypt, the pursuit by Egyptian forces, the coming of the "strong east wind" during the night and the exultant escape of the Israelites across the drained bed of the estuary, the subsequent abating of the storm and the destruction of the enemy detachment as the waters return. Later editing has so expanded the record as to make the event seem improbable; indeed, it is often represented in such a way as to seem impossible.[9] At the same time the thoroughly natural effort on the part of the biblical editor to underscore the miraculous nature of the event need not obscure its true proportions as a providential convergence of circumstances making possible the furthering of the divine purpose of redemption. It was, in short, "one of history's great, crucial, and destiny-filled accidents."[10] In its results it was meaningful enough, even to the eye unaided by faith's insight. What brings it home to the observer as being providential is the recognition that it was meaningful in the *intention* manifested through it. This intention is impossible to discern except through the eyes of faith.

Many other biblical miracles can be understood in this same way. For example, it is likely that many of the people watching by the Lake of Gennesaret when the fishermen, having put out into the deep and let down their nets for a catch, "enclosed a great shoal of fish" (Luke 5:1-11), saw in the occasion nothing more than a lucky throw the men made when a school of fish happened to come along. These observers viewed the event as spectators only and they interpreted it accordingly. On the other hand, the fishermen themselves saw in it nothing less than an authentication of the person and the message of Christ. And more than this, they realized that the pattern of Jesus' words and works had in the mystery of the purpose of God become interwoven with the pattern of their own lives. The real question posed by the miracle, then, was whether it was to be considered a special manifestation of God's will or simply a fortuitous convergence of circumstances. That Peter and his associates evaluated it correctly is confirmed by Peter's believing response: "Depart from me, for I am a sinful man, O Lord."[11]

This analysis points up the central and essential feature of the biblical miracle. In every case the real point of the miracles is the response of faith they are meant to call forth, not the process by which they were wrought. Jesus resolutely rejected the insistence that he give a "sign"—an objective, unmistakable evidence of the divine power at work. He knew that people who refused to respond to his ordinary works would not respond to extraordinary signs and wonders: "If they do not hear Moses and the prophets, neither will they be convinced if some one should rise from the dead" (Luke 16:31). The message of the miracle is nowhere regarded as discernible apart from the believing response of the individual and the community of faith in which he shares the life of God. Thus we see that one of the main reasons the modern person has difficulties with the miracles is that he usually asks a different question of the record from that which the record itself answers. His question—entirely proper and to be expected in a scientific climate—is, "How do they occur?" But the account exhibits less interest in this than in the response evoked: "And when they had brought their boats to land, they left everything and followed him." It is this disjointedness of modern inquiry and biblical answer which accounts for much of the confusion concerning the miracles. This is not to say that the modern question should not be raised in reference to the biblical account; it is only to insist that it be kept subordinate to the real intent of the record.

Study of the healing miracles of Jesus will disclose that his works of healing were wrought through the application of as-yet-unknown laws and methods of healing, laws and methods which have been in part independently discovered by modern science.[12] They were not aimless, spectacular, irrational displays of power. I remember as a boy pondering how Jesus must have healed the man whose ear Simon Peter cut off in that brief skirmish in Gethsemane before Jesus' real battle with the powers of darkness. In my youthful credulity it seemed to me that he must have reached down, picked up the severed organ and "put it back" in its proper location! Had this been the case, however, it would raise grave doubts regarding the reliability of the record and even the authenticity of the miracle itself. In reality, the record is everywhere chaste and restrained, not calling the reader to accept the utterly irrational and therefore not demanding of him a blind, unreasoning response. In this instance the event is described in a few carefully chosen words: "And he touched his ear and healed him." Mature judgment would suggest that he stanched the flow of blood from the open wound, not at all a spectacular marvel but the very least any competent physician would do.

It would appear that the over-all intention in the biblical miracles is not to exhibit a quality which ordinary happenings do not share. A miracle is rather an occasion in which "the essentially providential character of *all* events is made manifest in an especially clear and striking manner."[13] It is essential that this aspect of miracle be kept in mind. All reality, all history both personal and universal, has a miraculous quality about it. The acknowledgment of some events as being special illustrations of God's redemptive purpose helps us to see all of life subsequently in this light.[14] After all, which should be regarded as more "miraculous," for a sick child to recover from a high fever aided only by the prayers of an anxious parent or by an injection of penicillin administered by a skillful doctor? The question is not a rhetorical one; and the way one answers it will disclose the degree to which he has grasped the true biblical perspective.

The effect of this clarification is to set the miraculous element in Jesus' ministry in its true proportions. It is not by any means to devaluate it. Jesus intended for his miracles to reveal, not merely to impress; thus he cautioned those upon whom his works of healing were done to "tell no one about it." Nor does it mean that all his miracles can be accounted for as providential circumstances or as the application of yet-unknown techniques. In fact, every thought about the miracles of Christ should begin with the fact that he himself was a unique person. The Incarnation, along with the Creation and the Resurrection, stand in a class by themselves as having extraordinary revelatory power. They are what Pollard calls "singular" events and as such cannot at all be explained in terms of chance and alternative.[15] Jesus stood in a unique relation to God and also in a unique relationship to his fellow men. In truth he himself is the great miracle. It would be eminently incongruous to acknowledge the majesty and the mystery of his person and not recognize that there are inescapable elements of mystery about his works. And this applies to his present ministry as well as that recorded in Scripture. In the context of our discussion here the point is that there is no obstacle of scientific origin that need prevent our accepting the miraculous element in Jesus' ministry, not least because in a real sense the miraculous is indispensable to our understanding of Jesus himself.

Pollard summarizes the contrast between the scientific and the biblical criteria of events in terms similar to those we employed earlier regarding scientific and religious language:

> The more a given event has the power to reveal some timeless universal property of the world, the less it is capable of making manifest the hand of God in the shaping of events. And conversely, the more an event or sequence of events makes manifest the providential character of history, the more chaotic and fortuitous they will appear to those who seek only to discover universal law and order in history.[16]

Thus Galileo's discovery of the law of inertia yielded great new insights into the nature of inertia and of gravity, but in itself a freely falling body discloses nothing of providence. On the other hand the miracle of the Exodus was "a potent revelation of the power of Yahweh to save His people," but if we consider it purely objectively it appears as an event explainable through meteorological conditions and telling us nothing about history's universal laws. Every event, be it in the realm of physical, historical, or purely personal reality has this double-sided character.[17] It depends upon the event itself and the perspective from which one views it as to whether it will disclose more of order than of providence.

This dynamic view of the purpose of God makes it eminently possible to regard Jesus as a figure in history, subject indeed to the chance developments of life and the historical process—and yet triumphant over them. It has become quite prevalent of late to describe the gospel account as a drama and to regard our Lord as the central character in the working out of the drama of redemption. This manner of speaking has certain definite advantages, in that it enables one to steer clear of literalistic interpretations on the one hand and of the historical Jesus of liberal theology on the other. There is also an element of impressiveness about it that for the modern ear lends weight to the entire account. Yet this manner of speaking has certain perils also, chief of which is drawn from the very nature of drama. For drama does not allow of any continuing interpretation; it is fixed, once and for all. Each generation must simply take over *in toto* the figure dramatized. There is no need for the attempt to gain further light on the subject, for all available light has already been gathered. The result is a stagnation of attitude and effort which scorns as irrelevant whatever new light may be thrown upon it.

It is easy to see that this procedure is fundamentally unrealistic and untrue to the historical dimension. There will never come a time when new developments in contemporary history will not cast invaluable light upon past history, thus necessitating the continuing reassessment of received notions.

> No one thinks of bringing Shakespeare's Caesar up to date. The student of literature, whether he be philosopher, psychologist or moralist, deals with the immortal Roman depicted once for all in the play. But the biographer in contrast to the dramatist can never hope to pronounce a final word. Not only do new facts and facets disclose themselves, but also new biographers have been carried by the movement of life and thought to new points of view with fresh angles of vision.... As long as new history is being lived old history will require to be re-written.[18]

This dynamic character of historical involvement is an essential facet of the incarnate nature and work of Christ. Far from simply acting out the script of a divinely prepared scenario, he was content to face each moment squarely, fully aware of its gravity but with eyes wide open to its possibilities. He made chance his opportunity. For example, the record states that it was when John had been cast into prison that Jesus began to teach and preach. Why this occasion for launching his ministry? R. W. Stewart gives a simple answer: "One was down. Who would take his place? The entry of Jesus was quietly heroic and determined by the occasion. . . . He waited for the chance that made the way of duty clear."[19] Many an occasion of healing, many an unforgettable saying, was the result of a sudden emergency. Numbers of his most memorable deeds were done in response to the demand of the immediate situation. Just looking through the Gospels at random, we encounter such events as the paralytic lowered through the roof of the house, the storm on the sea of Galilee, the two blind men following him, the hungry multitude in the "lonely place apart," the young ruler who went away sorrowful, the woman at the well, Nicodemus the Pharisee who came by night, and many others. Such unexpected occasions and encounters seem far more like the chance occurrences that happen to one deeply involved in the to-and-fro of historical life than they do the successive steps of a drama being acted out. "Jesus lived in what George MacDonald calls, 'the holiness of the eternal now,' making life one long impromptu, improvising victory over every difficulty as he answered every questioner, and found a remedy for every bane."[20]

The crucifixion of our Lord is often spoken of as if it were deliberately planned by God, the inexorable working out of an eternal purpose of redemption. This, too, is a manner of speaking that must be employed with extreme care, since it could imply that Jesus had no choice in the matter. Scripture does indeed regard the death of Christ as being at the very heart of the redemptive purpose of God. But it does not do so in a way that implies a fixed inevitability. The path of Jesus led to Calvary because of his absolute adherence to the loving will of his father who willed that all men might be saved, not because he was foreordained to die hanging from a cross. Forces *in* history, not beyond it, were the factors immediately responsible for his grisly death: the proud opposition of the Jewish leaders, the weak vacillation of the Roman governor, the defection of Judas.

The highest manifestation of the purposeful action of God is seen in the fact that a historical defeat brought about by the interaction of many human wills and by the convergence of many chance circumstances became the means through which God redeems the world. Thus we must interpret the death of Christ in terms of both human and divine purpose, as Peter did when on the day of Pentecost he announced to the multitude: "—this Jesus, delivered up according to the definite plan and foreknowledge of God, you crucified and killed by the hands of lawless men" (Acts 2:23).[21] The latter part of Peter's declaration was evident to all who knew what had happened, regardless of their convictions in the matter, although they obviously could not have known its full implications. But that it was in fact the climax of God's eternal purpose to redeem his people—this is clearly the judgment of faith. What was the ultimate symbol of man's lost and forsaken plight is at one and the same time the ultimate sign of an unsleeping purpose. The same event, viewed successively from the objectively historical and then the theological vantage-points, yields a vastly different meaning. Yet neither view rules out the other. Both are necessary to the complete understanding of the event.

Such is the character of the purpose of God effectively working in this world. The events that occur in history and in personal experience can indeed be interpreted at the human level in terms of circumstances and human motive and act. But behind the circumstances, operating through the intricate maze of chance occurrences and alternative courses of action God is working out his master purpose. It is possible for one to go through life and miss it entirely, though even the man of dullest discernment can hardly help being impressed at times with the intricate relatedness of events. But if his eyes have been opened to the biblical perspective, time after time he will experience moments in which he feels the hand of God upon him. Again and again he will observe the Pattern emerging like an underground stream confirming his deepest and most precious conviction and, disappearing again, leaving behind the promise of the day to be fulfilled. And he will thank God, take courage, and continue on his way. ". . . We walk by faith, not by sight" (2 Corinthians 5:7).

Part Three

AN EMERGING WHOLENESS

Chapter VIII

The Scientific Setting

If the notion that physical reality has a firm, substantial character has turned out to be an illusion, even though held by the mind for the greatest part of man's existence, equally erroneous has been the assumption that physical reality comprises the main bulk of the universe so far as over-all volume is concerned. Up until fairly recently one was quite justified in holding to this idea, for the very good reason that no other alternative even suggested itself. However, with the rolling back of the horizons of knowledge which science has brought, this comfortable assumption has vanished. Actually, physical reality in all its forms constitutes only a minute fraction of the total volume of the universe. Both in its very small and in its very large manifestations, the universe is mostly empty space. Here and there an occasional particle of matter—here and there an occasional star or planet—but by far the major portion of observable reality is empty space. We live in what Sir James Jeans calls a "gossamer universe": Of empty nothingness there is plenty, but of solid material, very little.

This becomes much more evident to us as we turn our attention from the microcosm to the macrocosm, from the very small to the very large, although it should not be forgotten that the major portion of microscopic reality is empty space also. The tiny, terrible world inside the atom stands at one extreme of the physical order; the vast reaches of outer space with its billion-odd galaxies of stars and planets are at the other. As we have observed the witness in the infinitely small and its contribution to Christian truth, so now we turn to examine the knowledge natural science has gained about this majestic universe and its bearing upon the biblical message.

There is a striking parallelism between the development of fundamental ideas in physics and in astronomy. In each case we find that in ancient times there occurred a turning away from an earlier, more promising explanation of those areas of physical reality studied by the two disciplines to the acceptance of a scheme more suited to the level of the mind of the day. We have already seen how this took place in physics when Aristotle's categorical empiricism displaced the atomism of Democritus, with the result that the authority of "the Philosopher" was not broken until modern times and knowledge of the physical world began to progress. In astronomy the geocentric scheme of Ptolemy dominated the scene for nearly as long as its counterpart in the realm of physics. The interesting point is that the Ptolemaic explanation of the universe won the field over that of Aristarchus, who in the third century before Christ put forth the striking hypothesis that the earth revolves around the sun. As Archimedes reports it, Aristarchus affirmed "that the fixed stars and the sun remain motionless, that the earth revolves about the sun in the circumference of a circle, the sun lying in the middle of the orbit, and the sphere of the fixed stars, situated about the same center as the sun, is so great that the earth's orbit bears the same proportion to the sphere of the fixed stars as the center of a sphere bears to its surface."[1]

Examination of the above summary will disclose that Aristarchus had attained a generally correct understanding of the solar system and of the proportionately tiny size of the earth in the vastness of space. Moreover, his views were arrived at through sound scientific reasoning. Yet this scheme, which must certainly have been regarded as novel in Aristarchus' day, did not carry the conviction of his contemporaries. The Ptolemaic conception, propounded four hundred years later, remained well-nigh impregnable for centuries.

No scientific explanation can ever be accepted generally without the support and confirmation of experiment or observation. It goes without saying that the necessary instruments were simply not available in Aristarchus' day to bear out the accuracy of his highly advanced hypothesis. Nor was the experimental method by any means generally accepted in scientific circles, for that matter. It is not surprising that a less novel view prevailed. It should be noted that Ptolemy set forth the structure of the universe as common sense observed it to be: the earth at the center with sun, moon, and stars revolving around it in regular orbits, and the planets following more complicated paths. The Ptolemaic scheme had the support of "the appearances," and this is no small support to one who is as accustomed to relying on his senses as is man. In addition, the Ptolemaic account enjoyed the concurrence of the Genesis account of creation, literally understood.

There is no use arguing with history and doubtless it is unrealistic to imply that something else should have taken place than what actually occurred. But while we cannot change history, we can certainly learn from it. We see here another instance of the tragic stagnation of science caused by restricting knowledge to "familiar concepts." Admittedly, the truth must be expounded to each generation in terms which it can understand. Aristarchus was clearly too advanced for his time and therefore failed to carry the consensus of his contemporaries who were in fact more ready to accept the simpler Ptolemaic explanation. But this should be balanced with the recognition that physical science has progressed precisely at that point in its development when it has been willing to fly in the face of "the appearances." This fact should help overcome the inveterate tendency of the mind in every field, including theology, to fasten on familiar concepts simply because they seem right and sufficient to account for things as they are.

But while it was Ptolemy who got astronomy off on a sidetrack, it was Aristotle who kept it there.[2] The real enemy in Galileo's *Dialogue on the Two Chief Systems of the World* was the Aristotelian philosophy, spokesmen of which in Galileo's time defended Ptolemy against Copernicus. The magnitude of the task which Galileo and the other founders of modern science undertook is well stated by Alexander Koyré: "What . . . [they] . . . had to do, was not to criticize and to combat certain faulty theories, and to correct or to reduce them by better ones. They had to do

something quite different. They had to destroy one world and replace it by another."[3] The very existence of science as we know it
today is sufficient testimony to the success of their efforts.

Back on the original lines laid out by Aristarchus, astronomy
now began to make rapid progress in the exploration of the nature
of the physical universe. Confirmed by Galileo's observations, further explained by Kepler's laws of planetary motion, the Copernican scheme was joined into a consistent whole by the genius of
Newton. Newton supplied an ordered explanation of the entire
cosmic show by developing the idea that the planets are held in
their orbits by the familiar force of gravitation. On the basis of
this fundamental premise of a smoothly operating, clocklike universe, the horizons of astronomical knowledge were pushed
slowly outward and the true immensity of the universe was gradually impressed upon man's mind. We can appreciate the apprehension which gripped many men during the days when the
strange new story was unfolding, an apprehension which led even
a dedicated scientist like Blaise Pascal to exclaim: "The silence of
those infinite spaces frightens me." Clearly the universe was of
stupendous proportions, far vaster, far more complex, far more
mysterious than it could have possibly been imagined to be.

Just how vast it really is has not become fully evident until the
very recent past. The first step in the process was taken by Copernicus, who removed the earth from the center of the solar system
and placed it in a 93,000,000-mile orbit around the sun. It was not
until 1930 that the work of R. J. Trumpler at the Lick Observatory
occasioned a further removal. Trumpler demonstrated that the
solar system is not at the center of things astronomical as had
been thought, but is in fact some 30,000 light-years from the center of the Milky Way in a comparatively dim spiral arm. Measured in terms of astronomy the earth is nowhere in particular. It is
a minor planet orbiting about a star of medium magnitude located
in one of the billion or more galaxies making up the vast bosom
of the universe.[4]

Nearly everyone nowadays knows something about the magnitude of the interplanetary and interstellar distances, but it is
questionable whether the true scale of the macrocosm is generally

understood. Entirely new standards of speed and distance have had to be devised in order to speak meaningfully about these immensities at all. Even so, the speed of light and the concept of light-year are used purely as mathematical terms useful in expressing astronomical distance. Those who employ the terms make no claims of being able to *grasp* them.

Some comparisons by Bart J. Bok will convey at least some idea of the immensity of our own Milky Way galaxy. If we were able to travel at the speed of light, says Bok,

> it would take us only about one-seventh of a second to circle the earth, a little more than one second to go from the earth to the moon, about eight minutes to go from the earth to the sun, and about twelve hours to make a comfortable sight-seeing tour of the whole solar system, visiting all the planets. But at the same rate we would have to travel more than four years to reach the star nearest the sun—Alpha in the Southern Hemisphere constellation of Centaurus; and it would take roughly 100,000 years to pass from one end of the Milky Way to the other.[5]

This scientist goes on to point out that though the Milky Way contains more than 100 billion stars, the system is so enormous that only a very small fraction of the total space it occupies is taken up by the stars themselves. "We could readily store a million times as many stars in the present volume of the system without the risk of an undue frequency of stellar collisions."[6]

Anyone can observe for himself roughly what position our solar system occupies within the great wheel-shaped aggregation of stars that is the Milky Way. The center of the galaxy lies from the earth in the direction of the great constellation Sagittarius. As we look toward this, the brightest part of the Milky Way—best seen in summer—we are looking toward the far side of the great wheel. Here the density of stars is greatest and therefore the light brightest, so bright in fact that it is sometimes easily mistaken for cumulus clouds in our own atmosphere. As we look toward the weakest part of the starry concentration, which includes Perseus, Auriga, and the familiar Orion, we are looking toward the near rim of the galaxy where the density of stars is thinnest and the light correspondingly dimmer. The entire galactic formation resembles a mammoth Fourth of July pinwheel whirling about its central axis at approximately 140 miles per second. Yet even at this enormous speed it takes the sun and its family of satellites 200 million years to make a single swing around the center.

Through the new 200-inch telescope on Mount Palomar man can now see the almost inconceivably immense distance of two billion light-years into space. Millions upon millions of galaxies can be observed scattered throughout all this vast realm. These "island universes" themselves contain billions of stars, many of them much larger and of far greater brilliance than our own sun. It is entirely probable that a vast number of these stars possess planets. Astronomers are engaged in the study of the provocative and truly revolutionary question: Are we alone in the universe? At the new National Radio-astronomy Observatory at Green Bank, West Virginia, scientists are undertaking serious efforts to detect and record radio signals that may be emitting from other planets in the Milky Way.[7] It does not require much imagination to admit that there is plenty of room in the universe for other life and even intelligent beings like ourselves. The matter is not nearly as fantastic as it sounds. It poses a host of questions for the Christian consciousness, questions beyond our consideration at the moment. At the very least, we are made aware of the accelerating development of the science of the infinitely large and the stupendous possibilities it has opened to us.

The development of the modern understanding of the universe has not, however, been without fundamental modification. Science is an unwearying process of sustained investigation, and those who employ its aims and methods must be willing to lay aside basic assumptions when fresh information demands it. This was the case in 1887 when Michelson and Morley performed their famous experiment regarding the earth's motion. This experiment showed that one of the basic postulations of the Newtonian universe—the idea of an absolute space against the background of which fixed distances in space can be measured—was actually fictitious. The notion of absolute space and the corresponding idea of an "ether" through which light waves were conceived to travel were extremely useful as *assumptions*, and the data gathered with their help continues to be valid. But the Michelson-Morley experiment demonstrated that something was wrong with the fundamental assumptions, assumptions which affected vitally the over-all picture of the universe which science suggests. The outcome of this development was the theory of relativity formulated by Albert Einstein.

Briefly stated, relativity as it applies to fundamental astronomical concepts means that distances in space are never absolute, measured from a known, fixed point. They are always relative to a point chosen by an observer or to the observer himself. Furthermore, in determining the immense distances of outer space another dimension, that of time, becomes involved. Thus we arrive at Einstein's rather formidable but really very simple description of the universe as a "four-dimensional space-time continuum." This means that when an astronomer looks outward into the three dimensions of space, he is also looking backward in time, since the light from stellar bodies actually left those bodies a considerable time—perhaps millions of years—before. If, on the other hand, the astronomer selects a point in space—an earth, for example—then time becomes inevitably a variable in relation to all other points in space.

Suppose an astronomer were to try to communicate with the star Arcturus "right now." Since Arcturus is 38 light-years removed from earth and since radio signals travel at the speed of light, it would take 38 years for his message to reach its destination and 38 years more for a reply to come back to earth. In other words, "right now" is right now only to observers on earth where distances are terrestrial. The immense distances of the universe prevent us from extending that moment of simultaneity to any point in space other than our own earth. Scientifically speaking, it is impossible to transcend the human reference.[8]

The principle of relativity has revolutionized basic conceptions regarding the universe, and there are aspects of it that bear upon our Christian understanding of reality as well. As we turn our attention to the implications of this stupendous perspective for Christian thinking, we shall find that the principle of relativity is equally as significant as we found indeterminacy and complementarity to be. But first, we must deal with the more fundamental issue that appears the moment we turn away from the scientific setting to the Christian. In the light of what we have seen in this chapter, is there still a chance for genuine conversation between theology and natural science?

Chapter IX

The Christian Setting

At first glance there seems an utter incompatibility between the general picture of the universe we receive from science and that of the Bible. The Scriptures begin with the basic declaration, "In the beginning God created the heavens and the earth." When confronted by the vista we have just described, one cannot have his roots deeply embedded in the Christian tradition and fail to ask: "What does this declaration mean today?" It is a question of first importance, one that will not tolerate facile attempts to "reconcile" the two perspectives into a religious scientism or justify a preoccupation on the part of Christians with an exclusive "religious" or "biblical" concern that closes its mind to science. In order for any solution to be considered satisfactory, we must face squarely the central issues involved, maintaining the integrity of both the biblical and scientific perspectives.

The very least demanded is a disciplined "stretching of the mind" that will enable us to comprehend the fantastically transformed cosmological outlook that is becoming part and parcel of the thought-world of this present time. We should have no difficulty expanding the physical aspect of the biblical view of "the heavens and the earth" to the modern concept of "the universe." While the biblical cosmology is different from the scientific, it is beyond question that by "all things" the writers of Genesis meant "the created universe." Through the analysis of light reaching the earth from the stars, astronomers have determined that the stars are constituted of the same elements that compose the earth's physical structure. Whatever may be the size and the distance of the stars and other planets from us, their base elements are the same as those of earth. The universe is physically homogeneous.

The word "universe" itself can be a fruitful source of confusion here, for the very reason that we think we understand it readily enough. Yet it will have a variety of meanings to different observers. The word is derived from the Latin *universum*, from *unus*, one, and *vertere*, *versum*, meaning "turned into one"— therefore one whole or system. To the common man "universe" denotes the aggregate of all existing things; to the student of Scripture, the whole of creation. To the man of science, however, the meaning is much more complex. In the manner of the ancient Greeks he may entertain the notion of an orderly cosmos, but we have seen that this rational concept appears to be no longer tenable. Some insist that man himself turned the landscape of his reality into one whole or system, making the notion of "universe" in effect a man-originated idea. It is probably too early in the game for scientists to give a clear, agreed-upon definition to the term, and we shall do well not to be dogmatic. Let it suffice here to denote by "universe" the modern scientific understanding of the infinitely large, the latest data regarding the stars, planets, and galaxies. That data is still coming in, but the basic proportions of the astronomer's vista can be discerned with reasonable clarity and definiteness.

The question that confronts us is, simply: Is the biblical point of view tenable in the face of the magnitude of the modern vista? It is by no means a foregone conclusion that an astronomer will be moved to worship when he beholds the majesty of the heavens. The psalmist sang,

> O LORD, our Lord, how majestic is
>   thy name in all the earth! . . .
> When I look at thy heavens,
>   the work of thy fingers,
>   the moon and the stars which thou
>   hast established . . .
>
> Psalm 8:1,3

But the psalmist had already found God in his own experience and he was simply beholding the confirmation of that encounter writ large upon the face of the heavens. This condition, by the way, must always be considered the cornerstone of an authentic Christian outlook upon the physical universe. The perspective upon which we have insisted all the way through these pages must be extended into our comprehension of the infinitely large. The question is not, Can we find God in the majesty and order of the macrocosm?, but, Are our Christian convictions concerning reality adequate to the magnitude of the modern understanding of the universe?

The validity of Christian convictions regarding reality has always been a subject to stir debate. The authenticity of personal religion is one thing, and Christians have been distinguished by the intensity of their personal conviction: "I know whom I have believed . . ." The primacy of personal religion, the personal appropriation of the fatherhood of God through Jesus Christ, is the very heart of Christianity. But it is something else when one then turns to interpret reality from this personal orientation of faith. It is here that difficulties arise. Before the age of Copernicus most Christians considered the conviction that the earth was the center of things to be part and parcel of a meaningful personal Christianity. Indeed, for many thousands of years man thought he lived at the center, and he had no good reason to think otherwise. The earth appeared stationary enough, and the heavenly bodies moved with martial regularity across the skies above. Had this been questioned, it would in most minds have been tantamount to an outright denial of God. Yet, viewing the situation in the perspective of history, we can see that such was not the case. Christianity survived the displacement of the earth from the center of things with comparative ease. It is no longer a matter of concern that the sun is the center of the solar system, not the earth. In the same manner, Christians of bygone days considered it essential to regard the universe as having come into existence in the space of six days. When with the advent of geology the immense antiquity of the earth became apparent, and the arrival of man upon the scene was shown to be evolutionary in nature, many mistook this to mean the overthrow of the Christian view by an infidel science. This mistaken view has not been completely overcome even yet, but in the minds of most Christians of intelligence the findings of geology do not present a stumbling block.

Some have seen in the accumulating knowledge of science itself the destruction of genuine Christianity. This was the view of W. T. Stace, who in 1948 published his famous article in the *Atlantic*.[1] Stace's contention was that science has destroyed the sense of purpose in history and in all reality. Since a sense of purpose has distinguished the Christian view of things, then Christianity itself is dead.

> Religion could survive the discoveries that the sun, not the earth, is the center; that men are descended from simian ancestors; that the earth is hundreds of millions of years old. These discoveries may render out of date some of the details of older theological dogmas, may force their restatement in new intellectual frameworks. But they do not touch the essence of the religious vision itself, which is the faith that there is a plan and purpose in the world . . . The essential religious spirit . . . cannot survive destruction of belief in a plan and purpose of the world, for that is the very heart of it. Religion can get on with any sort of astronomy, geology, biology, physics. But it cannot get on with a purposeless and meaningless universe.[2]

Fortunately, however, Stace has confused the biblical conviction of purpose with the Aristotelian concept of final cause.[3] His critique actually does not reach the Christian view at all; it only reaffirms what was already evident, namely, that the notion of final cause was an anthropomorphic construction that science has long since proved to be gratuitous. Far from being "killed" by science, the biblical conviction of purpose can be attested by numerous suggestive instances from both physical and historical reality.[4] These are not sufficient to prove demonstratively the existence of a plan, but to the candid believer they are testimonies to the purpose of a God apprehended by faith in Jesus Christ as the climactic Event of all history. Although not certain demonstrations, they are signs of his purposeful work, mute messengers of God.

Genuine Christian faith has never really depended upon the scientific accuracy of prevailing cosmological views. Whenever it has done so, it has by that very fact betrayed a radical deficiency. Thus the amalgamation of Christian doctrine and Aristotelian science into the *Summae* of Thomas Aquinas now appears to be one of the worst misfortunes that could have befallen the Christian cause. Likewise the opposition to evolution in the name of "what the Bible teaches" was an unhappy convergence of pseudo-science and biblical literalism. Christianity has demonstrated its ability to survive the displacements in thinking that have come about through scientific progress in spite of the difficulty of abandoning cherished "familiar" notions.

It must be recognized that we now stand on the threshold of another displacement, more radical than either the Copernican or the Darwinian. The Christian consciousness is being called upon to acknowledge that its understanding of reality has been far too domestic, far too terrestrial. That there are other planets in the universe similar to our own, that there is life on them, that there are other intelligent beings like ourselves, that they may have histories not unlike our own, that there may have been revelations of the divine nature and purpose comparable to that recorded in the Bible, that the purpose of God is far vaster than anything we have thought or imagined—these are now distinct possibilities with which we must learn to live.[5] Their practical effect is at present almost nil, it is true, but they do affect vitally the success with which we shall be able to continue regarding this universe as God's universe.

Throughout the Christian era men have often comforted themselves with the idea that the universe was created primarily for man's sake. Even when it was not affirmed explicitly, it was not infrequently assumed; and reasons for the assumption are not hard to find. The tremendous event of the Incarnation itself seemed to support it; and, in addition, the geocentric universe that men knew for so long appeared to bear it out. At the same time, in its best moments Christianity has insisted that man's good must always be subordinate to God's glory. The two are not antithetical, it is true, but there is in the Christian perspective a definite priority. "Man's good" may include a multitude of aspects and facets of man's total experience. But the Scriptures affirm in unmistakable terms that in the fullest sense the "good of man" can come only as he seeks to "glorify God and to enjoy Him forever." This paradox is absolutely essential to the entire Christian concept of values, as well as to the practical experience of humble Christians who have found it to be true. The stupendous vistas of astronomy now, quite unexpectedly, confirm it. Surely it would be a colossal absurdity to insist that the universe as we now know it was called into being purely for the well-being of man, purely to serve the purposes of the planet Earth.

At the same time, the uniqueness of this planet and of man himself are also indisputable. Measured in terms of physical stature and value, it goes without saying that both the earth and its human inhabitants are mere nothings, specks of matter in the vast sea of emptiness that is the cosmos. But measured in different terms, we reach a different conclusion. Insignificant as the earth is when compared with other planets of the solar system, it is probably the only planet in that system capable of supporting life as we know it. So many conditions—involving atmospheric balance, temperature, plant life, rotation and tilt of its axis, and numerous other factors—are necessary for life and personality to exist as they do on the earth that it must be recognized as being a truly exceptional planet. And it goes without saying that the uniqueness of man himself is intellectual, moral, and spiritual rather than merely cellular.

This debate has been a fascination to man throughout his existence and no one has put it more reverently and accurately than Blaise Pascal in the famous Fragment 72 of the *Pensées*. Having contemplated the majesties of the infinitely large and the intricacies of the infinitely small and reflecting on man's median position in the physical order, Pascal asks,

> For in fact what is man in nature? A Nothing in comparison with the Infinite, an All in comparison with the Nothing, a mean between nothing and everything. Since he is infinitely removed from comprehending the extremes, the end of things and their beginning are hopelessly hidden from him in an impenetrable secret . . .[6]

Pascal then goes on to show elsewhere that this fact of man's "disproportion" underlines the Christian conviction that his true worth and being cannot be measured in purely physical or even intellectual terms. A true understanding of man and his actions within the worlds he inhabits must come from another source and be based on another criterion. And this is so because "man infinitely transcends man."

It would be easy at this point to leave the shores of established fact and launch out into the deep waters of speculation. Some have done so, usually without much real edification. Some years ago I heard a popular speaker expounding the idea that Christ intended the Great Commission to include the other planets in the universe and that Christian missionaries must be prepared to man space craft to bear the gospel to the outer galaxies!

Certainly an excess of imaginative sensationalism was joined with a minimum of sober realism in such a judgment. We cannot be dogmatic in either direction about such matters. It will be better if we let the overwhelming mystery and majesty of the modern view of the universe move us to humility. Actually, whatever arguments are advanced supporting the existence of life on other planets can be neatly balanced by opposing arguments. Nature is prodigal in her waste. This planet was uninhabited by any kind of life for billions of years. Man has been here only an infinitesimal period compared to the entire history of the earth. If we let the approximate time since creation be represented by one 24-hour span, the life of man upon earth has covered only about the last 22 seconds of that period. We are clearly dealing with questions we cannot answer; but, the mind of man being what it is, we cannot help asking the questions.

The important thing is the fact that there is nothing in our present basic understanding of Christianity that need be regarded as incompatible with the contemporary scientific perspective. Many are skeptical when they confront the amazing disproportion between cosmic setting and terrestrial purpose. They question whether omnipotence needs a setting so vast for a result so small. But here again, can we confine the "result" to the planet Earth? And even if we do, are we safe in denying cosmic signifi-

cance even to terrestrial purpose? Certainly science has taught us
not to accept the merely credible because it appears to us to be
so. This is, as we have seen, the very essence of anthropomorphism
and the denial of true science. Once more Galileo's "irreducible
and stubborn facts" must be the criterion, not philosophical judgment.

Admittedly the challenge is a vast one. It throws up into
bold relief the real thrust of James Denney's aim expressed earlier
in these pages: "to help you to be true to all you know, and at the
same time to keep a complete and joyful faith as Christian men."
Yet it would seem that there is a point where language in the ordinary sense loses its meaning, certainly to a great degree. It
should be no more "difficult" to accept the existence of a Creator
"adequate" to today's universe than it is "difficult" to accept the
staggering conception science gives. In fact, almost the opposite
is true. The ancients affirmed that knowledge begins in wonder;
in the present context this order may well be reversed and the
wonder that a dedicated scientist, or any reasonable man for that
matter, experiences as he contemplates the facts may mean that
he is "not far from the kingdom" (Mark 12:34).

One of the fundamental aspects of the biblical teaching is that
God's acts are conditioned upon no other ground than his own
will. It was of his will that he chose Abraham and his descendants, forming them into a "holy nation," a peculiar people set
apart for the achievement of a purpose that became progressively
clearer with the unfolding of Old Testament history. Again and
again, the people were reminded that it was not of their goodness
that they were chosen; on the contrary, the aim of their call by
the sovereign Lord of history—so the prophets reiterated—was to
issue in a goodness which would be a blessing to all men. They
were *chosen* by the free, gracious act of God, and this sense of
mission was to be the chief aspect of their religious consciousness. This purpose was realized in the coming of Jesus Christ, the
incarnate Son, and in the new Israel, the new humanity gathered
by faith in his name. It is clear that the meaning of what J. B.
Phillips describes as God's personal visit to the planet Earth must
be understood in these same terms. That such a visit has been
made is a fact to which the cumulative evidence of human expe-

rience testifies; the significance of the visit for the life and destiny of this planet itself is set forth in the pages of the New Testament. But it must be acknowledged that its full meaning against the cosmic background that is the contemporary scientific setting is not as yet clear to us. In fact, it may never be.

As imposing as the difficulties are, however, a careful study of the scientific evidence will disclose that in some points there has been a convergence of the biblical and the scientific perspectives rather than an opening wider of the traditional gulf between them. There are at least two facts that support this generalization. In the first place, the modern scientific view gives reasonable evidence for believing that the universe may not be infinite. As long as the concept of "absolute space" was current, there seemed no way of denying that the universe was of infinite extent in all directions. Any idea of "the universe as a whole" was meaningless because no significance could be attached to the idea of wholeness itself. In this kind of situation it is easy to see how difficult it would be for one to accept creation in the biblical sense and remain on speaking terms with science.

But with the elimination from scientific terminology of the concept of absolute space and the acceptance of the principle of relativity, there appeared reasonable basis for believing that the universe can be a *uni-verse* after all and not just a physical order of infinite extension. Evidence now points to an expanding finite universe rather than to an infinite universe. Galaxies are not fixed in their relationships to each other, but are receding at speeds proportional to their distance from each other. Those galaxies twice the distance from the Milky Way are receding at twice the speed of those galaxies only half as far. Space is curved in all directions, roughly like the surface of an expanding balloon.

> A soap-bubble with corrugations on its surface is perhaps the best representation, in terms of simple and familiar materials, of the new universe revealed to us by the Theory of Relativity. The universe is not the interior of the soap-bubble but its surface, and we must always remember that while the surface of the soap-bubble has only two dimensions, the universe bubble has four—three dimensions of space and one of time.[7]

Thus there are no straight lines in the universe. A beam of light setting out through space from a certain point would not travel on and on indefinitely for an infinite distance. It would describe a great cosmic arc, returning to its point of departure in approximately 200 billion years. This is indeed an enormous circumference, and it goes without saying that it is arrived at through mathematical computation rather than experimental demonstration. But the important point is that the beam of light would return, very much like a traveler setting out on a round-the-world tour will eventually arrive back at his jumping-off place.

Modern science describes the universe as "finite but unbounded," summing up in this designation the latest insights. While the Christian point of view is not dependent on the scientific terminology, it would seem to us permissible to make use of that terminology to clarify and illumine the Christian conviction further. From this point of view the emphasis falls properly on "finite"—creation is "unbounded but finite." In a real sense, therefore, the meanings of "universe" and "creation" tend to converge at this point, and the Christian finds an added measure of confirmation that the universe is genuinely a created universe. We need regard ourselves no longer as confronted with an inescapable and difficult dilemma of how an infinite universe can be a genuine *creation*—even if created by an infinite God.

In addition to the fact that we can now with reasonable scientific probability accept a finite universe, the modern view also supplies evidence that the universe is not eternal. One of the most exciting developments of recent times is the fact that for the first time in history science has something to say about the age of the universe. Throughout most of history there was nothing really definite for science to offer on this subject, except that the universe may be eternal. But this was an assumption very much on the order of the assumption of absolute space. There was no need to think otherwise and no evidence to support any other view. Within the last decade and a half evidence has been growing which indicates that the universe did in fact have a beginning. At present there is an astonishing amount of scientific detail about how the beginning must have occurred.

Three separate lines of evidence point to a beginning, and the three are remarkably convergent. One of these comes from calculations concerning the decay of radioactive elements in the earth's surface, another from the rate at which nuclear fuel "burns" in the sun, and a third from the use of the Doppler effect or "red shift" to measure the rate at which galaxies are receding from each other.[8] Extensive work has been done in this field in the last few years and the figures are repeatedly being revised. We shall do well not to be too exacting about the figures; nor do we need to base our case on the latest hypothesis. The *fact* of a beginning for the universe in its present form now seems scientifically justified; for our purpose the actual age itself is a matter of secondary importance.

Nor do we need to enter the debate between those astronomers who espouse the instantaneous theory of creation as expounded by Le Maitre and those who hold to the more recent idea of a continuous or "steady-state" creation championed by Bondi, Hoyle, and others.[9] We shall see shortly that "creation" in the biblical view is not primarily a physical concept anyhow and therefore is not linked necessarily with any theory of astronomy concerning the origin of the universe. Even though it will be recognized that the Genesis account seems more compatible with the instantaneous theory, we must not make the mistake of identifying the two. Once again it is a matter of perspective, and for the sake of the integrity of both the biblical and the scientific point of view we must continue to keep them separate. The fact of utmost significance—a fact which we have had before us all through these pages—is that what astronomy is now saying about the universe is beginning to shape up as being not at all incompatible with the essentials of the Christian setting.

A universe of stupendous proportions and of incredible age but nonetheless finite and temporal—this is the general picture that modern science sets before us. The idea of the expanding finite universe has not *ipso facto* solved all the major questions regarding the macrocosm. There is still a prodigious amount of research and reconnaissance to be done. The Christian mind must apply itself to all the questions this expanded vista poses for the

Christian cause. But it is significant to realize that, vast and perhaps insoluble as these problems are in the light of present knowledge, they can be dealt with in the context of—at the very least—a scientific "perhaps" instead of a categorical "impossible."

But we may ask: Is this not really the general picture we should expect to find when we have made the biblical account of God and the world part and parcel of our thinking? That unknown writer who first set down those amazing opening words of Genesis could not possibly have realized the physical magnitude and scope of what he was saying. No doubt he would find the modern vista as mysterious and overwhelming as we have. Yet it is not at all beyond reason that, having familiarized himself with the scientific information, he would say in effect, "That is the way it ought to be, to have been created by the God I know."

> I raised my eyes aloft, and I beheld
> The scattered chapters of the Universe
> Gathered and bound into a single book
> By the austere and tender hand of God.[10]

The chapters are vastly more numerous and the book a billion times larger and longer, but the hand of God is still the same.

Chapter X

A Basic Compatibility

These considerations bring us to the position where we may turn our attention constructively to the Christian doctrine of creation. Fundamentally, creation means the same thing today it has always meant in the Christian scheme, namely, that God is "Maker of heaven and earth," Creator of "all things visible and invisible." But clearly the understanding gained from science will bear profoundly upon the way we regard it. If we examine the biblical story of creation in the light of modern science, we shall see at least two things of paramount importance. In the first place, information gained through scientific research supplies a reasonably adequate description of how the creative process occurred. Second, and even more important, the scientific account has the effect of throwing up into clear relief the biblical doctrine in its true relevance and power.

Here we see one of the most significant contributions science has made to theology. It is a widely held and popularly accepted notion that science has weakened and undercut the Genesis story. Well-meaning persons, regarding the two accounts as contradictory, have done their best to "reconcile" the two, thinking to reach a rational basis on which both may be accepted. Such attempts are all the more pitiable because unnecessary. Science does not contradict Genesis; it complements it. Science seeks only to determine *how* the process occurred; it is not within its province to determine by whose agency and for what purpose it was accomplished. These are—as they have always been—convictions of faith that supply ultimate meaning to the entire process.

Throughout a major portion of history Christians have looked upon the Genesis account as being the literal truth of the way the world came into being. When science began to plant doubts in Christian minds about the accuracy of the Genesis story, some put forth the idea that the concepts of Genesis were "prescientific," because formulated before the scientific view of reality made its advent. But this view also proved to be unsatisfactory, for it tended to undermine the relevance of the entire Bible as well as dismissing what was true in the Genesis story itself.

It is certainly beyond our intentions in these pages to recount the unhappy and bitter quarrels that have flared around this complex matter. However, we think it may be relevant to recall that Christians and others accepted for so long the Genesis account, not because literal belief in that account is necessary to the message of the Bible as a whole, or even of the book of Genesis as a whole, but simply because there was no creditable scientific account to teach men otherwise. Archbishop James Ussher's chronology, which set the date of creation at 4004 B.C., was reasonable enough when we remember that up until then there had been no serious critical study of the text of the Bible and the background out of which it came. Even as late as the seventeenth century it was customary to begin a book dealing with the history of the world with a chapter describing its divine creation.[1] If we have become accustomed to thinking in scientific terms, it is salutary to recall how recent these terms were in making their appearance.[2]

Modern biblical scholarship is coming to understand the first eleven chapters of Genesis as an introduction to the entire Bible. These chapters consist of a series of great parables that reveal the fundamental truth about man as he stands in relation to his Creator. The meaning of these stories must be sought on a different plane than that of history or sociology. The truths they record are independent of any particular point in time or of any particular place in history. Creation is not dealt with here from the scientific side at all; and if we wish to understand this account, we must read it not as "a chronological, astronomical, geological, biological statement, but as a moral and spiritual conception."[3] The impor-

tant and essential message is the *meaning* of the creative historical process and of human existence itself, not the scientific explanation of the origin of all things. The meaning of such a stupendous occurrence as the creation of the universe, the true place
of man in creation, the way evil grips a man and tempts him to
fall into sin, the way societies and cultures exalt themselves to
the point of defying God himself—the existential, transhistorical
meaning of such fundamental matters is best conveyed in a story,
a parable.

> A parable is a story which may or may not be literally true
> (no one asks whether the Good Samaritan ever literally 'hap-
> pened'); it conveys a meaning beyond itself. It implies that be-
> yond the words of the story which our outward ears have heard
> there is a meaning which only our spiritual hearing can detect:
> 'he that hath ears to hear, let him hear.'[4]

Thus the aim of the Genesis account is to exalt God, by whose creative Word the whole universe came into existence, and also to
awaken man to a sense of creaturely dependence. This is *ultimate*
truth, the truth about man and about all reality as they stand in
the dimension of divine relationship.

To cite a simple example, in the original Hebrew the name
for "Adam" is not a proper name at all; it is a generic term meaning simply "man." For the meaning of the story of Adam and
Eve we must therefore look beyond the superficial procedure of
locating the two as our first parents. The message of the story
is far more direct and unsophisticated than that. For we are all
"Adams" and "Eves," and the pattern of our sinfulness is the same
as theirs. It is with us as with them: our creation by a good and
gracious God, our commission to useful service in his world, the
enjoyment of his favor, and a way of life that brings happiness
and peace. But—now as then—doubt is implanted, disobedience
occurs, and anxiety and dread are the result, joined with the
miserable "knowledge" of moral failure. The point is that *our*
rebellion is like theirs, *our* excuses sound strangely like theirs;
ours is the guilt and the resulting moral impotence.

The stories are told in such manner that when I read them, I realize that I am not reading an account of history; I am looking in a mirror! This is not Adam I am reading about; this is myself. This is not a tower built long ago in a faraway country; this is my own society in action, and I am part and parcel of that society.[5]

Certainly it should be said that this is the way humble Christians have read and understood these passages anyhow. They have gone to them primarily for their religious meaning, not for their scientific accuracy. However unscientific were the Christians of the past in interpreting the creation passages as literal history or science, the fact remains that they have helped to nourish the Christian heart. At the same time, there is no doubt that much trouble resulted from failing to distinguish their parabolic, existential character.

Rudolf Bultmann has faced squarely the fact that science makes it impossible for us to accept the biblical view of the world, that is, of the physical world, and he insists that it is necessary to "de-mythologize" in order to understand the Bible. But as we have suggested before, in pressing for a consistent existentialist interpretation Bultmann would lead us too far. Who is bold and competent enough to undertake the process by which the biblical view of the world is extracted from the biblical perspective as a whole? Not only man himself but man's *situation* is, in the biblical setting, portrayed in the existential dimension. Therefore we would "de-mythologize" at our peril; better to let the message come to us in its full proportions—"three-storied universe" and all. Then let us ask, in the context of modern ideas: What does this mean for us?

A note of caution ought to be added also. There is a definite change of tone as we begin the twelfth chapter of Genesis. While the message of the record is still not to be sought in its historical or scientific details, beginning with the story of Abraham the account takes on a definitely historical character. On the other hand, the first eleven chapters are "epic" in their scope.[6] The ages of the characters are elongated. Long periods of time are subsumed in a few words, and the account clearly does not move within historical lines. It is possible that the stories receive their inspiration at least in part from an historical background. There is fairly general agreement, for example, that the account of the Tower of Babel received its inspiration from the building of the great ziggurat at Ur of the Chaldees. Likewise, the story of Noah probably had its genesis in an historical setting. But in these introductory chapters history is incidental; and this not because they have *no* relevance to history but because they belong to *all* history.

It is therefore hardly necessary to regard the Genesis account of creation as literal truth in order to obtain its true meaning and relevance. Understanding it in the manner we indicate, we find that it speaks far more pointedly to our situation than if we encumber it with scientific or historical shackles. With his tongue in his cheek, a friend of mine maintains that the "great fish" really did swallow Jonah. His meaning, of course, is that the repeated attempt to interpret the book literally meant that in some circles its real message was lost. Likewise with the Genesis story: In the measure that we have defended Genesis as science, we have not infrequently surrendered its true meaning as revelation.

> Unless I know that I am created by God, am utterly dependent upon him, am responsible to him and am judged by him, the creation of the world will be for me only a philosophical speculation (even though I may regard it as intellectually the most satisfying hypothesis about the world's origin and *raison d'être*) or merely a 'dogma' of the Creed (even though I may assent to it as the teaching of the Church). To know that God made *me* (and *therefore* all the world) is to understand the parables of creation aright . . .[7]

To miss *this*, while engaged in the battle to "defend" Genesis against science, is tantamount to surrendering the real message of the book for a pseudoscience that satisfies neither our scientific nor our religious sensibilities.

The central idea of the biblical doctrine of creation is the imparting of existence through a sovereign act of the divine will. This idea is expressed in the fact that God creates "through his

Word." The divine Word is the means of creation: "And God said, 'Let there be . . . ,' And there was . . ." Christian theology has expressed this distinctiveness in the doctrine of *creatio ex nihilo,* creation out of nothing.[8] Here again it should be borne in mind that the real thrust of this basic principle is not scientific in nature. It expresses the faith "that all things come from God, on Whom they absolutely depend for existence and meaning."[9]

The Old Testament mind was concerned almost entirely with the question of religious destiny and meaning. The Old Testament people had encountered God in their own history and personal experience. It is to be expected, then, that when they came to express their faith in the universality and omnipotence of God, they should do so in story form, not in the abstract formal terms of science or philosophy. Even if the Genesis writers had had the means of writing a strictly scientific account as we know it today, their readers would not have had the faintest notion what they were talking about. It is the vantagepoint, the perspective, of Genesis that supplies its appeal and power, not the literal accuracy of its detail. This is the incomparable uniqueness of the biblical story: It supplies the vantagepoint which gives ultimate meaning to the process science is now in some measure able to describe. This position is summed up in that primal affirmation we have had occasion to discuss already: "In the beginning God . . ." This declaration at once establishes the indispensable basis upon which the history of redemption recorded in the Bible can be understood, and it also affirms the radical dependence of all reality upon its creative source. It rules out from the very beginning any notion that the universe is self-sufficient, that it evolved according to a purely natural development, or that any part of the creation itself might be considered divine. There is a clear demarcation between Creator and creature, Creator and creation. At the same time, the account reiterates time and again the fundamentally benevolent purpose of creation: "And God saw that it was good." The origin of evil is left a mystery, where it must ever remain. But while its origin is left in mystery, the fact of evil is bluntly and vividly depicted: "Did God say, 'You shall not eat of any tree of the garden'?" Even in these early pages, however, the redemptive intention of God is graciously recorded. Though the consequences of man's sin are cosmic in scope ("Cursed be the ground for thy sake"), the history of redemption is prefigured in the divine dealings with Adam and his descendants. The backdrop of all history and human experience is thus sketched in with bold strokes—the indispensable conditions which men of all ages must accept and understand if they are to comprehend creation aright.

The very practical result of this discussion thus far is that in our thinking about creation we should *from the beginning* consider God as related to the creative process. Men have been tenacious in their determination not to accept this order of things. They have clung to the outworn, obsolete notion that somewhere, sometime they will happen upon the evidence, or they will construct the argument, or they will find the frame of reference that will give objective assurance of God, and give meaning to reality and experience. They have hoped to find God and the ultimate meaning only he can give at the *end* of the process of research and reasoning. But the best of Christian history fairly trumpets the lesson that whoever would find God at the end must have accepted him at the *beginning*. There is literally no other way. And when we follow this order, we find that far from being an irrational demand, this approach gives us the very condition upon which true rationality can be achieved.

Faith is often popularly and even seriously understood as a "leap in the dark." But, on the contrary, while faith inevitably contains an element of risk and mystery, it is more properly to be regarded as the acceptance of that *arché*, that vantagepoint which gives light and meaning. "By faith we *understand* . . ." says the writer to the Hebrews (Hebrews 11:3, italics mine). Insofar as we have been unwilling to accept this order of thinking in its full biblical intent, we have not infrequently fallen victim to some lesser faith-principle that could not give us what we needed.

This means further that science itself is, in a genuine sense, a religious activity. How could it be otherwise in a universe created by God?

> I want to be able to look at science, its methods, its presup-
> positions, its basis, its splendid successes and its austere disci-
> pline; and then I want to be able to say: Here is God revealing
> Himself for those with eyes to see.[10]

Exactly. And such a position leads us beyond the point where
we must defend the Bible against science, beyond the point where
we try desperately to cling to some local or "hedgehog" defense
or put our confidence in a "God of the gaps."[11] From this lofty
position we can truly understand the impatience of a man like
Max Planck who insists that the "problem" of theology and
science is a "phantom" problem. Seen from this height, it appears
as just that.

A deeply reverent scientific description of the way the creative process may have occurred has been given by William G.
Pollard in an essay entitled "The Cosmic Drama."[12] Pollard's
work has been beneficial to us already in these pages, and this
present contribution is another example of the light he has shed
upon the problem involved in relating the scientific and biblical
perspectives. Pollard combines the neutron capture theory of element formation worked out by George Gamow with the known
actions of nuclear physics to relate the way the universe came
into being.

According to this account of it, at the moment of beginning
some four billion years ago there appeared a vast cloud of neutrons at enormously high temperature and in rapid expansion.
Since neutrons characteristically break down according to a process of radioactive decay into protons and electrons, and since this
radioactive process consumes ordinarily about 13 minutes, a large
proportion of the existing elements could have been formed
within that very brief span of time after the beginning occurred.
The expanding and cooling cloud of neutrons then began to con-
dense into "droplets" which were in fact atomic nuclei. This
process of universal expansion and radioactive cooling resulted
in the abundances of the various elements existing in the entire
universe. Some of these elements, such as beryllium, lithium, and
boron, continued to react with other nuclei, and this accounts for

their scarcity today. On the other hand, we still have instances of the radioactive changes that went on during the original expansion. These are found, of course, in the quantities of uranium, thorium, and potassium that still remain in the physical world and in which radioactivity is presently found.

Pollard theorizes that the stupendous release of energy set in motion by the expanding mass of gas and nuclear dust gave rise to tremendous "local" storms or hurricanes. These great whirlpools, of enormous extent and marked by incredible turbulence, were the "progenitors of our present day galaxies," now on the average of 2 million light years apart.[13] Smaller centers of turbulence within the nascent galaxies gradually contracted and through nuclear reactions caused by high temperatures and increasing density, formed into stars and clusters of stars. Even smaller centers, too small to sustain a nuclear reaction, condensed into planets moving in orbit about a major condensation associated with them. The earth itself was one of these planets, reaching approximately its present size after about 500 million years had passed. Continuation of radioactive decay beneath the earth's surface brought on an increase in temperature and the corresponding volcanic and mountain-building activity familiar to students of geology. Release of gases trapped within the turning earth gradually issued in the atmosphere and the condensation of water vapor into drenching rains formed the oceans. Elsewhere in the universe other galaxies, stars, and planets, were presumably undergoing the same process of formation and development.

During all this incredibly long period of "slow, almost imperceptible development," Pollard goes on, there was no life, no part of creation capable of "apprehending it, appreciating it, or of responding to the mighty power which had brought it into being."[14] Only after an immense span of time and, even so, still over a billion years removed from us, did the first life appear in the warm, primeval waters. It appeared in "some way which we do not understand" out of the complex store of organic materials which had been slowly accumulating in the growing oceans. As time went on, this elemental form of life slowly developed into numerous varieties of both sea and land animals. Finally, after

millions of years of more change and development, and of the
appearance of new and more complex species of life, one of the
new species which appeared was man. And with his advent, "the
mysterious cosmic drama had at last produced something as a
part of the created universe itself which could apprehend, appreciate, and know something about the existence and structure
of that universe." There had come into being "a center of consciousness" which was capable of "responding in awed wonder
and appreciative understanding to the Almighty Author of this
majestic and marvelous drama of creation and evolution."[15]

Pollard depicts the creative process as a profoundly meaningful and moving drama in which the appearance of man forms
the climactic point. It is related with obvious reverence and—
important for our purpose in these pages—with scientific precision. This is especially evident in Pollard's frankness concerning
the present state in scientific knowledge of the way that life came
to be. It appeared, he notes, "in some way which we do not understand." Scientists are at present engaged in the attempt to
synthesize life in the laboratory; and if they are successful, their
findings may throw valuable light on the manner in which it
originally came into being. Some people have expressed the fear
that a scientific success at this point would deal religion and
theology another mortal blow of the kind that evolution is supposed to have delivered. But this fear only reveals the fuzzy
state of thinking we still find in many quarters today regarding
the real relationship between theological and scientific truth. Is
it not true that theology and natural science both endeavor to
describe things that happen in the same world? And since this
is so, is it not likely that what they tell us may at first glance seem
antithetical but will, with deeper study, be seen to be two sides
of a single whole? The fear in question stems from the mistaken
notion that theology and the Bible supply the whole truth of the
origin of life, when in reality they tell the story of life—and centrally human life, of course—from the ultimate perspective of
relationship to God. When Christian spokesmen insist that the
Scriptures give the whole story, they should not be surprised to
hear scientific echoes making the same claim for science.

Indeed, we need not accept Pollard's account as final; but it is sufficiently reliable to accept it as factual. Many scientists themselves find it deeply disturbing and unwelcome; they prefer to have the universe back on "its old comfortable basis," minus the challenge of implied purpose or meaning. But what is this but another instance of science setting before us as persons and as societies the necessity of decision? For, Pollard concludes, there are only two ways of viewing the cosmic drama. One is the secularist view, which is "man-centered and turned inwards on itself." The other is the Judeo-Christian view, which centers attention on God, taking the "fact of the occurrence of this drama, the wonder that this particular universe should have been created at all, the marvel of its majestic splendor and dramatic development, as the central fact of all existence."[16] Thus Pollard brings us to what is no less than the point of convergence of the scientific and biblical perspectives. The scientific description itself does not supply us with an answer to its meaning; it confronts us with a choice. And the choice brings us face to face with the fact of the Christian revelation in the Scriptures and in Jesus Christ.

Pollard's concluding words put this inescapable decision superbly, and we cannot do better than to make them our own conclusion in this section:

> The choice between these two viewpoints is a crucial decision for each one of us. To the thoroughgoing secularist the Judeo-Christian view is pure folly, a vestigial remnant of primitive superstition, a wholly meaningless and unnecessary surrender of man's rightful and proper biological function, which he holds in common with all other living species, to wrest from the world the best he can achieve for his own welfare, comfort, security, and glory. If he is right, there is no cosmic drama at all; there is only matter, motion, energy, and change. But to the thoroughly religious person the record is high drama, intensely personal, and charged with meaning, purpose, and significance. If this is actually the true view, then we, who are unavoidably involved as crucial and determining participants in this drama, surely become guilty of sin of the most terrible magnitude

against its Author, when we ignore the drama . . . for our own satisfaction and glory. And so this choice is really a very grave decision, one not to be taken lightly at all, but to be worked out with fear and trembling.[17]

The same choice, it is true, has been before every other generation to which the biblical message was directed. But it is neither inaccurate nor irreverent to say that it has never stood out in such bold and inescapable relief as it now does. Far from having shown the biblical account to be irrelevant or false, the scientific information only facilitates the restating of the biblical truth with fresh meaning and power. On the one hand, there are indeed "matter, motion, energy, change," and the life of frustration and settled banality that results when there is nothing more than these; on the other hand, there is "the high drama, intensely personal . . . charged with meaning, purpose, and significance" of the life of fellowship with God. Without a doubt it is the ultimate choice.

Chapter XI

Invitation to Sanity

It may come as something of a surprise to some to learn that there is more—much more—in the Bible about creation than what we find in the first few chapters of Genesis. In fact, if we consider it in its over-all proportions, we shall find that "creation" is in the Scriptures a most comprehensive and fertile conception. The larger significance of creation is essential if we are to appreciate its importance and its relevance to the modern scientific setting. In this larger sense the scriptural idea of creation conveys the truth that this is "our Father's world," and is in essence an invitation to sanity as well as to sanctity.

In the first place, we should note that both the creation accounts given in Genesis emerged out of the history of Israel. Biblical scholarship has determined that the "P" or "priestly" story (that given in Genesis 1:1-2:3) was put into its present form after the Exile and that it reflects the general outlook of the priestly group in Judah. On the other hand, the "J" narrative (Genesis 2:4-25) was compiled before the Exile and represents the outlook of the prophetic mind. The two accounts present interesting variations, variations which help us to understand the respective points of view of these two groups in Israel. But the paramount fact about them is that they agree in affirming creation *from within* history. The fact of creation is thus not to be considered a direct revelation of God, unconditioned by historical contingencies. It was, rather, an essential component of both the prophetic and the priestly mind.

As we have seen,[1] the Old Testament people had encountered

God in their own experience both personal and historical, and it was this encounter that led them to affirm God's creation of all things. We find in the Scriptures, therefore, that creation is essential to an adequate understanding of history and of human experience generally. Creation is, in fact, the larger backdrop against which history and the entire existence of man are set. The prophet's plea for righteousness was not infrequently made within this context and receives a large degree of its weight and sanction from it. The following passage from Isaiah is an illustration of the way the prophet's message was related to God's creative purpose:

> For thus says the LORD,
> who created the heavens
>   (he is God!),
> who formed the earth and made it
>   (he established it;
> he did not create it a chaos,
>   he formed it to be inhabited!):
> "I am the LORD, and there is no other"
>
> Isaiah 45:18.

This entire passage, chapters 43 to 45, is a powerful declaration of the prophetic message against the background of God's creative activity. Since he formed reality to be a true universe rather than a chaotic coalition of insensible and senseless powers, then the life of Israel and that of all the nations should be patterned according to his will. How stupid—and how sinful—to turn the world into a jungle when God created it to be a garden! Thus creation supplies the answer to man's profoundest need, the need to know that there is meaning in life and in history and that both men and societies are held responsible for the use they made of God's endowments.

The scientific and cultural spheres of man's existence are from the outset made subordinate to the moral dimension. The fundamental categories in which life is to be understood are those of judgment and grace. Man is commissioned to be the steward of creation: ". . . Fill the earth and subdue it; and have dominion

. . ." (Genesis 1:28). But this stewardship extends far beyond the animate and inanimate creation itself; man is first of all to be a steward of his own life and conduct: "You may freely eat of every tree of the garden; but of the tree of the knowledge of good and evil you shall not eat, for in the day that you eat of it you shall die" (Genesis 2:16b-17). In this refined symbolism the fundamental dimensions of man's freedom are carefully defined: Man is free to enjoy the benefits of God's world, but he can do so only as he remains God's servant.

This intimate connection between creation and moral obedience is expressed in several of the Psalms, among which the 24th is especially noteworthy. The psalmist begins with an affirmation of God's creative ownership:

> The earth is the LORD's and the
> fulness thereof,
> The world and those who dwell
> therein;
> for he has founded it upon the seas,
> and established it upon the rivers.

Having set this background, he immediately makes an inquiry that is ethical in nature:

> Who shall ascend the hill of the LORD?
> And who shall stand in his holy place?
> He who has clean hands and a pure
> heart,
> who does not lift up his soul to what
> is false,
> and does not swear deceitfully
>
> Psalm 24:1-4.

This is no narrow moralism, but a recognition of the genuinely moral character of creation. The reverent contemplation of "the manifold works of the Lord" and a consideration of the wisdom in which they have been made moves the believing mind to the deeply personal prayer:

May the glory of the LORD endure
 for ever,
  may the LORD rejoice in his works . . .
May my meditation be pleasing to him,
 for I rejoice in the LORD

                              Psalm 104:31, 34.

The same theme is reiterated in Job, whose testimony we have
already considered. Whatever the misery and apparent mean-
inglessness of Job's estate, the answer to his situation was to be
found in a believing acceptance of God's sovereignty. And while
some will insist that this did not really answer Job's problem, it
is undeniable that there is healing—even for our deepest hurts—
in stopping and considering "the wondrous works of God" (Job
37:14).[2]

Throughout the Scriptures the working out of God's purpose in history is seen against the background of his purpose in
creation. The doctrine of creation therefore gives the Christian
faith its basic thrust and meaning. ". . . It lays the foundation for
the unique biblical understanding of our finite, historical life."[3]
When we remember that science cannot speak with any competence on these fundamental matters, then the power and relevance of the biblical doctrine again appear.

At the same time, we have been careful throughout these
pages to insist that this fundamental meaning of the created world
is not a human discovery. While the doctrine of creation is affirmed from within history, it is a conclusion drawn from the revealing action of God within the historical process and not the
end product of a rational, scientific inquiry. Science may speak
of the beginnings of the universe, but in the strict sense *beginning* is not to be equated with *creation*. We know reality to be
created because the Creator has revealed himself to faith.

Since, in the larger context of the Bible, the climactic point
of revelation is the Word made flesh, there is thus a definite relationship between creation and incarnation. The creative principle has been disclosed in a truly human life. To know the Creator not only as sovereign creative power and immanent presence,
but supremely as manifest in the flesh—this is the distinctive

message of the New Testament bearing on the subject of creation.

If we are led to inquire about the mysterious Being whose creative processes brought us and all things into existence, we reply that his nature is revealed in Jesus Christ. If we wonder at times what the selfless love of the Savior and his faithful disciples can accomplish in a world so deeply beset by tragedy and sin, the answer is that this love is the same as that which created the universe. If we separate creation from incarnation, as some would have us do, then the Power that fashioned this universe in its vastness remains a wholly other, a "cold and forbidding mystery, and life is dominated by fate, by sin, and by death." Conversely, the love we behold in Christ is only "the pathetic frailty of a defeated liberal."[4] The union of power and love—this is the larger meaning of the doctrine of creation. So Paul puts creation and incarnation together in a truly monumental text:

> . . . it is the God who said, "Let light shine out of darkness," who has shone in our hearts to give the light of the knowledge of the glory of God in the face of Christ
>
> 2 Corinthians 4:6.

This same association is made in the prologue to the Gospel of John. There has always been an inclination in biblical studies to identify the Logos doctrine of John's prologue with that of Philo, the great Alexandrian who attempted to bridge the gap between Hellenistic thought and the Old Testament. John's terminology and his use of the Logos are admittedly similar to the concept of Philo, but closer examination confirms the conviction that John was not using "logos" in the Philonian sense. As James Denney put it, "Though he borrows the conception, he does not borrow from it."[5] The background of John's use of Logos is none other than the Old Testament notion of God's word as his creative energy. John employs it to set forth the record of a life in the flesh which can be explained only by the relation of eternal sonship: "And the Word became flesh and dwelt among us, full of grace and truth; we have beheld his glory, glory as of the only Son from the Father."

We find therefore in the larger biblical setting a definite parallelism between God's creative and his redemptive work. Redemption is not merely moral reformation; it is a new beginning, a radical new orientation. Salvation is being "born anew," it is the making alive of those who "were dead . . . (in) trespasses and sins"; the man in Christ is "a new creation." Life in Christ is a continuing process of putting to death "the old man" and putting on "the new"; it is walking in the "good works, which God prepared beforehand, that we should walk in them." The love that redeems—calling into existence a person with a genuinely new outlook and scale of values—is the same as that which called the universe into being and which sustains it through the aeons. As creation is a divine work, so is redemption; and in this intimate parallelism lies the dynamic of the Christian religion.

In this larger perspective the universe is regarded as the unfolding of the mind of God in Christ. In his teachings Jesus frequently drew attention to factors that are inherent in the very structure of reality and which are no less than attributes of God himself. He reminded his hearers of the dependability of God's world: "Do not be anxious . . . but seek first his kingdom and his righteousness, and all these things shall be yours as well." He appealed to basic, self-evident truths: "A sound tree cannot bear evil fruit, nor can a bad tree bear good fruit"; "the earth produces of itself." He employed illustrative parables drawn from the familiar yet abiding realities of life: "A certain man had two sons"; "A certain man went down from Jerusalem to Jericho." In every possible way he sought to bring home the truth that life can be meaningful because we are living in a world created by God and thus undergirded by the very character of God.

Further, Jesus appealed to the impartiality of nature's processes as a basis for understanding the goodness of God. This is one of the most difficult aspects of human experience; it would seem at first thought that God ought to favor some, especially the weak, the poor, the virtuous, the innocent. Yet a moment's reflection will reveal that he could not do so without producing veritable bedlam on earth. The earth is a home, but it is also a school. "God who loves us does not temper the wind to the shorn lamb . . . Rather he makes his sun to shine upon all alike—and all can feel its warmth."[6] Therefore Jesus could urge his disciples to love even their enemies, for the love patterned after the Father's is not conditioned upon those loved. "Love is not love which alters when it alteration finds."

In the same vein our Lord taught that the universe is inevitably biased toward good, that evil is self-defeating and therefore doomed. He admonished men to "rejoice and be glad" when they were "persecuted for righteousness' sake" (see Matthew 5:12, 10), for the future reward would far outweigh the present distress. "In the world you have tribulation; but be of good cheer, I have overcome the world" (John 16:33). Christ recognized full well the presence and power of evil in the world; he frankly warned his followers that they would encounter suffering and possible death. But he insisted that evil's sway is only temporary and is in fact under God's control: "You would have no power over me unless it had been given you from above" (John 19:11). Evil is a bound power; it may bring a cross, but it cannot prevent the resurrection that follows. Our Lord did not endeavor to account for the mystery of evil. In reply to the disciples' question on one occasion, he said, "It was not that this man sinned, or his parents, but that the works of God might be made manifest in him" (John 9:3). He exhorted them, as he exhorts us, to employ the very conditions that make the presence of evil the deepest mystery of all—the fatherhood of God and the dependability of God's world—to overcome evil in its every expression.[7]

Creation thus reaches its climactic point in Christ. The cosmic drama comes to its fulfillment in him. The five to ten billion years of pre-human history take on ultimate meaning and importance when we realize that they were preparation for the full disclosure in history of the nature and will of the Creator to the creature who alone has the capacity to understand and to enjoy his creation with him. And, correspondingly, the true majesty and splendor of the revelation in Christ can be seen only as we view him against the background of the aeons of time and the immensities of space that become known to us through science. Christ is thus the measure both of the glory of God the Creator and of the significance of man the creature. In the bosom of a universe that envelops him, in the midst of a reality that startles him by its magnitude and its mystery—a reality that gives him the means to destroy himself if he chooses—there comes a message of infinite appeal and power: "God was in Christ reconciling the world to himself" (2 Corinthians 5:19).

The apex of the biblical perspective is found in those awe-inspiring passages that speak of Christ being the very mediator of creation itself. "All things were made through him, and without him was not anything made that was made" (John 1:3). God "has spoken to us by a Son, whom he appointed the heir of all things, through whom also he created the world" (Hebrews 1:2).

> He is the image of the invisible God, the first-born of all creation; for in him all things were created, in heaven and on earth, visible and invisible, whether thrones or dominions or principalities or authorities—all things were created through him and for him. He is before all things, and in him all things hold together. He is the head of the body, the church; he is the beginning, the first-born from the dead, that in everything he might be pre-eminent
>
> Colossians 1:15-18.

A sense of discrimination, derived from the study of the Scriptures as a whole, would counsel us not to regard such passages as simple paeons of praise, designed to magnify and exalt the person of Christ. They have a concrete significance, inseparable from the larger creation perspective. That Christ is the master "clue" to the meaning of this created order, that faith in him unravels the mystery of existence, that commitment to him supplies that wholeness of life and thought that creation itself implies, that he is the perfection of creation, that his coming was the aim and the intent of the Creator, and that creation truly "belongs" to him—this is at least a small portion of the wealth contained in these passages. Inseparable from this is the further truth that Christ is the master "clue" to the *renewal* of this created order. The conquest of sin, evil, and death has begun in him; the reconciliation of all the broken elements of the family of God is effected in him within the community of his followers, the Church. Thus Paul speaks of God's plan "for the fullness of time, to unite all things in him, things in heaven and things on earth" (Ephesians 1:10).

In Christ we know that the Creator is "the Father of lights with whom there is no variation or shadow due to change" (James 1:17). The infinite steadiness of the divine purpose is expressed centrally in the biblical concept of God's righteousness. The full meaning of the Hebrew word, *hesed*, defies translation. It is closely akin to "faithfulness," but this does not begin to exhaust it. The RSV translators employ "steadfast love" and this, while being somewhat prosaic, is nevertheless marked by its accuracy. It is the steadfast love of God, his infinitely compassionate faithfulness of purpose in which lies the meaning of Christ and also the meaning of the fact and the history of the physical universe.

A further facet of the biblical view of creation is that of the unity of man with physical reality. Man was created out of "the dust from the ground." His sin brought a curse upon inanimate reality as well as upon himself; "cursed is the ground because of you." But just as the consequences of man's sin are felt through the physical order, so do the results of man's redemption extend even to the physical realm.

It would be tempting at this point to fall back upon the outmoded distinction between "religious" and "cultural" or "scientific" and affirm that the eschatological teaching of the Bible is entirely "religious" (or in Bultmann's term "existential"), having no real reference to the physical order and the prospect which science forecasts for it. But once again it is a matter of a twofold perspective rather than of two sets of information having no relation to each other. Science does indeed testify that there will be an end of all things, at least as far as the planet Earth and our solar system are concerned, either through the eventual burning out of the sun or through the "scorched earth" that will result if the sun explodes into a *nova* or *supernova* such as have been observed in other galaxies in recent years.[8] In the light of this possibility, by the way, the picture of the dissolving of the elements in 2 Peter 3 is not at all a sensational one. Physics bears its own witness to the basic uncertainty that besets the physical order, as well as to the truth that "with the Lord one day is as a thousand years, and a thousand years as one day" (2 Peter 3:8). Stable and secure the sun and its family of planets may appear to be, but the latent dynamism that is at the very heart of physical reality could bring an end to it all in a flash.

At the same time, it would be as great a mistake to interpret this teaching of Scripture as scientific fact as it was to regard the parables of creation literally. Whatever may be the time and the nature of the end, it is abundantly clear that the main thrust of the biblical perspective is the molding of character that will survive every catastrophe, even the ultimate one; "Since all these things are thus to be dissolved, what sort of persons ought you to be in lives of holiness and godliness . . . !" (2 Peter 3:11). The final destruction of this physical order as we presently know it— whether it be immediate or remote—is thus called in to give added sanction to the patience and trust necessary to genuine Christian discipleship. This is true of more proximate and common catastrophes as well. The scriptural writers give no support at all to those overly pious slackers who would withdraw from active service to wait for the end.[9] But they regard the impermanence of the physical order as the ultimate refutation of materialism as a way of thought and action. The illusion of terrestrial security must never become an excuse for idleness or license on the part of those to whom God has given "all things that pertain to life and godliness" (2 Peter 1:3).

The biblical hope for this world has two facets, both of which are necessary if the whole is to be understood adequately. The conviction of ultimate triumph is paramount. The tension between present and future is a real tension for one who dares to take the biblical message in all seriousness.

> The creation waits with eager longing for the revealing of the sons of God; for the creation was subjected to futility, not of its own will but by the will of him who subjected it in hope; because the creation itself will be set free from its bondage to decay and obtain the glorious liberty of the children of God
> Romans 8:19-21.

This great poetic image is strikingly analogous to those majestic parables of Genesis. It teaches that man's redemption will mean also the redemption of nature from decay and death.

> If we believe that in Christ there is incarnate the Logos through whom all things were made, we must also hold that all things, and not sentient beings alone, find their true home in him.[10]

Creation is thus an unfinished process. In some way too vast for our comprehension, man's total environment—that is, the universe in all its parts—will share in man's redemption. In its present state creation is characterized by suffering and death. Its struggles, its aspirations, its frustrations, its yet-unsolved mysteries ("nature red in tooth and claw") all have a place in the vast cosmic process by which God is bringing into being a new state of existence marked by spiritual freedom and the harmony of man with man, and man with nature. Thus the drama culminates in the bringing into being of "new heavens and a new earth in which righteousness dwells."

Unlike the scientific prospect, the biblical perspective is radiant with hope and promise. No doubt we must maintain a reverent agnosticism regarding the precise meaning and shape of the future denouement. But one cannot confront the universe in its vastness and its variety without being struck by the almost infinite possibilities open to a resourceful Creator for the fulfillment of the terrestrial purpose of redemption. Reinhold Niebuhr's phrase "indeterminate possibilities" is a good summation from man's point of view of what our thoughts regarding the future should be.[11] In the majestic imagery of Scripture the victory of God's purpose and the fulfillment of all that now exists is triumphantly anticipated. Paradoxically, the creation—having been pronounced good by its Creator—yet must await the ushering in of the future glory before it can share in unqualified perfection. Faith itself shares in this redemptive tension:

> . . . and not only the creation, but we ourselves, who have the first fruits of the Spirit, groan inwardly as we wait for adop-

tion as sons, the redemption of our bodies. For in this hope we
were saved. Now hope that is seen is not hope. For who hopes
for what he sees? But if we wait for what we do not see, we wait
for it with patience

Romans 8:23-25.

Equally as important as the conviction of the ultimate triumph
of God's purpose is the other facet of the biblical hope for this
world, namely, the assurance of the present reality of the Kingdom in history. God's work in Jesus Christ has released redemptive forces which have changed radically the face of human society and which are still at work among us. The influence of Christ
and the Church upon the social, economic, and cultural life of
man no doubt belongs to the realm of the intangible and is impossible to measure either in extent or degree. But there is no
doubt as to its reality. Not through an inevitable progress erron-
eously thought to be scientific because based on a scientific principle, but through repeated invasions of the divine into history,
through the creative fermentation of Christian ideas, through
humble ministries of reconciliation carried out by those, great
and small alike, who are constrained by the love of Christ does
the life of the Kingdom make its impact upon the world. In judgment and forgiveness repeatedly administered through the events
of history and personal experience, the people of God are brought
to repentance and freshly committed to the task of witnessing to
the headship of God in Christ. Thus in the very center of history's
stream there moves the Church, the redemptive community con-
tinually renewed by grace and re-engaged in the task of the ages.

A universe in which the love of God can find full expression,
in which Christian faith and discipleship are vindicated and revealed in their ultimate value, a universe in which Jesus Christ
and his Church are truly at home—this is God's true aim and
purpose, the final destiny of this created order. Whether we interpret this cosmic climax as a "far-off divine event, to which the
whole creation moves," or whether we regard it as an imminent
denouement does not really matter. The important thing is the
triumph of God's purpose and the fact that all may share in that

triumph who fulfill the necessary conditions. And those conditions are "Whosoever will, may come." Or, in the familiar summary of the biblical message given by John, "God so loved the world that he gave his only Son, that whoever believes in him should not perish but have eternal life" (John 3:16).

Established and kept in that promise, therefore, it will not be presumptuous but of the very essence of faith itself to conclude this main body of our study in the conviction that whoever responds to the invitation, in addition to experiencing the present reality of the Kingdom, will in the end witness and share in the final perfection of all things created, the dramatic completing of the cosmic story which began with that event announced in those monumental words: "In the beginning God created the heavens and the earth."

> For still the vision awaits its time;
>   it hastens to the end—it will not
>   lie.
> If it seems slow, wait for it;
>   it will surely come, it will not
>   delay
>
> Habakkuk 2:3.

Conclusion

In all likelihood, one's first impression upon having had his attention directed to the subject of this book is that the "problem of theology and science" has died down considerably in importance, especially in view of the more immediate problems of biblical authority, Christian unity, nuclear warfare, world peace, and the like. This impression is strengthened by the fact that at the present time there seems to be no specific point of contention between theology and natural science, such as the structure of the universe or the origin of human life. A more adequate appraisal, however, will confirm the conviction that the problem has in our time become vastly more serious than before. In the intervening years since Galileo and Darwin the traditional chasm between theology and natural science has, if anything, widened and deepened.

By and large, both theology and natural science have for some time now regarded each other with a circumspect aloofness. Instead of an occasional eruption—which at least had the merit of establishing communications, unsatisfactory though they were, each is prone to ignore the other completely, as if it did not even exist, and to proceed in its inquiries entirely on its own, using its own presuppositions and methods and occupied with its own problems. The result in the minds of thoughtful observers is that of an even more profound divorce than existed during the heyday of the Copernican or the evolutionist controversies. In fact, the traditional "conflict" has not at all been settled, even though it is true that both theologians and natural scientists occasionally speak nowadays in terms more compatible with each other than before. What has happened is that the setting of the conflict has simply been transferred from the study and the classroom to the pew and to the man on the street. Many a sincere Christian with scientific training and background who deeply desires to worship God intelligently and to serve him with an up-to-date commitment feels himself to be of divided mind. What he hears in church often has no relevance to the secular current in which he swims. Theology holds no attraction for him, not because he is uninterested but because he frequently fails to note any point of contact between theological doctrines expounded—or perhaps ignored—from the pulpit and truth arising from other sources.

That this is an intolerable situation hardly needs to be said. Theology and natural science exist in the same world, the world which the New Testament describes as the Christian mission field. It is inconceivable therefore that there should be a permanent and irreparable divorce between two such important disciplines of mind and heart as these are. That is, unless we are unwilling at the outset to grant that each has ample justification for existing and that each deals with truth important for man. In fact, this is manifestly the only basis on which we can begin to think about a relationship between the two at all. But once each has made this basic concession to the other, we are inevitably confronted with the chasm between the two. The mind of man being what it is, we cannot rest satisfied with such a dichotomy. Nor can the Christian remain content that a vast area of human thought and life continues to move ahead largely unrelated to the basic Christian perspective given in the Bible.

In the modern world there has, it is true, come about an appearance of harmony between theology and natural science. Very few informed people nowadays will accept the thesis that Christian thought and scientific thought are at fundamental variance in their understanding of reality. We have moved beyond the evolutionist controversy and the infamous "monkey trial" of 1925 to see that what distinguishes scientific understanding from Christian understanding is the point of departure, the frame of reference. There is today a greater readiness to recognize that science and theology each has its distinctive point of departure in understanding reality and that each of these is legitimate and necessary. In addition, there appears to be a deepening awareness among some theologians of the immense importance the relationship between the two will have in shaping the thought of the future.

At the same time we must not mistake a cessation of hostilities for a truly lasting peace. It is one thing to acknowledge the probability that there really is fundamentally no conflict. It is quite something else to believe that there is a *positive relationship* between theological thought and scientific thought and to determine the character of this relationship. In the contemporary situation, any attempt to deal with the problem at this deeper level is hindered on the one hand by an obsolescent impression of hostility inherited from the past and encouraged by such influential volumes as Andrew D. White's *A History of the Warfare of Science with Theology,* and on the other hand by a theological world that, for the most part satisfied with older approaches and solutions, chooses to ignore the problem and give its attention to other matters.

The world today is increasingly under the dominion of science. The advances of science have been nothing less than phenomenal. Scientific methods and achievements have had almost universal impact upon life and society.[1] The modern world finds itself enlarging its control over its environment, more and more skilled at organizing to combat disease and lengthen human life, and through scientific methods and techniques in the service of good will increasingly able to solve many distressing problems of social and international proportions. While humanity faces the distinct possibility of nuclear annihilation through human miscalculation or overt aggression, this possibility has not at all slowed the advance of scientific progress. It has only spurred on both East and West in the race for world supremacy through scientific achievement and control. Half the human race is under the domination of an ideology which dogmatically asserts that science has superseded Christian theology, the latter (so it is claimed) having now become obsolete through the inexorable unfolding of the historical process. The other half, while not asserting it as bluntly as the first, nevertheless finds itself sorely tempted to make science its chief patron and the products of science its chief good.

The growing catholicity of the scientific point of view thus poses one of the most serious challenges before informed Christians today. It is not too much to say that the success of the attempt to make the Christian message understood and received in today's world must be judged in large part by whether or not we can formulate a positive and promising approach to scientific understanding. The recognition that science is no savior is in itself not adequate; beyond the acknowledgment of need there must be the positive assurance that help is available and that it is not inconsistent with the proven facts and principles that science has established.

No doubt the situation facing us is complex as to its causes, and it would be easy to oversimplify the reasons lying behind it. But there are at least two important facets of the problem that offer themselves as being responsible in great part for the modern isolation. One of these pertains to the course of theological development in the recent past. Coincident with the rapid strides made by the sciences in the last one hundred years and more, churchmen have tended to retreat within the realm of the purely doctrinal or biblical as for them the area of primary and even sole concern. Partly on the defensive against what appeared to be a hostile science and partly because of internal disagreements concerning the nature of biblical authority and the attempt to discover the historical Jesus, Christian thinkers were generally unwilling if not actually unable to keep abreast of the rising tide of secular knowledge. During the last part of the nineteenth and the early twentieth centuries the sphere of theological discussion was conceived by one influential school of theology to be limited strictly to the "religious" as distinguished from the cultural or scientific. Thus there developed a "split-level" type of thinking reminiscent of the "natural-supernatural" division dear to so many medieval spokesmen of the Christian faith. In fact, when Karl Barth broke with the dominant liberalism of the early years of this century, he carried this cardinal principle of the Ritschlian school over into his own formulation. On the point that theology has a limited area which constitutes its sole sphere of concern and competence Ritschl and Barth are agreed, no matter how strongly the latter repudiated the former's position during his early days. It is striking how James Denney's most telling criticism of Ritschl in 1895 applies just as directly to Barth in 1962. Said Denney:

> Christian theology is not a separate department of intelligence, having no connection with others; just because it is a doctrine of *God,* it must have a place and recognition for all those impressions and convictions about God which have exerted their power in man's mind, even apart from the perfect historical revelation.[2]

Denney is pleading here for a crucial feature that must characterize Christian thinking in a world created and upheld by the sovereign God, namely, that Christian thought stands in essential relation to *all* the contents and problems of thought and life. Obviously, the Christian thinker's first task is to understand the historical revelation in Scripture, but it is a mistake to think that this can be done without any reference to information and truth received from other sources.[3]

What distinguishes a Christian thinker is that he be able to interpret truth—all truth—from the point of view given in the historical revelation in the Bible, not that he be a specialist in an already overspecialized society. The charge of imperialism is all too easily leveled at that theological specialist who, having confined himself to a rearrangement of traditional doctrines according to his own personal orientation or that of his particular "school" of thought, then dares to venture outside his own premises. Fortunately, there is growing recognition of the need for clarifying the place and the task of the Christian thinker in the modern world, but the hour is already late and there is still much to be done. For the inevitable outcome of this retreat from the world of culture on the part of Christian thinkers has been a twofold one. Not only did Christian spokesmen forfeit the privilege of speaking relevantly to the cultural world; they also denied themselves the benefit of pertinent information being gathered by the sciences.

It is hard to measure the ground that has already been lost by the theological world in its dealings with the information science has gathered about the physical world. Christian theology has been nowhere as inept as in its attitudes toward the advances of science. It may not be obvious at first glance, but practically every advance in scientific thought has had the effect of reducing both the adequacy and the importance of Christian interpretations of reality as these interpretations have been traditionally understood. On the whole, it cannot unfairly be said that the story of modern science and technology has been the story of a shrinking theological relevance.[4] Some of the most significant achievements in scientific theory can be seen now to be liberating influences, theologically speaking, rather than the destructive opinions they were thought to be by many at first. The heliocentric view of the solar system and the theory of evolution, to mention only two, have given a far more majestic concept of the universe and of the creative process. Yet they were bitterly opposed when first propounded. Christian theology has regarded all too many of the advances of science in such hostile manner. It has maintained what C. A. Coulson calls a "series of hedgehog positions" in its defense against the scientific attack. It has relied on the "God of the gaps" only to have its confidence rudely shaken when the "gap" was found to be scientifically explicable after all. All the while, we are warned, "the enemy is pouring his energy and his forces into the region behind us."[5]

In defense of the theologian, it should be said that within the setting of today's scientific world we are apt to forget that it was only recently that science gained the unqualified right to be heard. Science is still a youthful movement. For a large part of its history it did not have anything like the universal acceptance it enjoys today. Luther's dismissal of Copernicus' theory of planetary movement as "the overwitty notion of a Fool" may seem inexcusable enough to a modern observer. But the attitude of the great reformer becomes a little more understandable when we note that in Luther's day experimental science was still in its infancy, while the Ptolemaic theory of the universe had been almost universally accepted for 1500 years and more.

Be that as it may, it is evident that the situation is radically different today. In the modern world the scientific approach enjoys an authority very nearly that of dogma, and it has impressive accomplishments to support its bid for competence. The very success of science confirms the truth and validity of science. Certainly this is so in the minds of a majority of our contemporaries, and we are persuaded of its truth in fact as well, insofar as the pragmatic test will allow. Thus the burden falls on Christian spokesmen to testify to the necessity and the adequacy of the Christian point of view in the midst of a situation not only heavily influenced by science but in large measure actually brought about by science. It is no longer possible—if it ever was—for the thoughtful Christian to take refuge in the "religious" or the "dogmatic" or even the "biblical" as in any permanent way isolated from the whole range of human thought and experience. Eminent thinkers such as Gilson, Whitehead, Butterfield, and others have demonstrated how Christian ideas made no small contribution to the rise of the modern scientific movement. But what of the contrast between the obvious successes of science on the one hand and evidences of theological stagnation on the other?[6]

Along with this general retreat from the world of culture and natural science on the part of Christian theology, there still persists in many quarters a fundamental misunderstanding of the nature of scientific knowledge and the uses to which it can legitimately be put. During the course of the development of modern science there were some who employed scientific information and insights in the attempt to "prove" the truth of the theistic or the biblical point of view. Lecomte du Nouy and A. Cressy Morrison may be cited here as two modern examples of the many who have through the years fallen victim to this admittedly attractive temptation. Du Nouy argues that "the logical and rational consequences" derived from "the scientific capital accumulated by man" will "lead inevitably to the idea of God."[7] Morrison contends that "so many essential conditions are necessary for life to exist on our earth that it is mathematically impossible that all of them could exist in proper relationship by chance on any one earth at any one time." From this he concludes that "there must be in nature some form of intelligent direction. . . . there must be a purpose."[8]

It is easy to understand how this way of dealing with the problem can be so readily accepted in the popular mind, conditioned as it is to seeing in the "scientific" point of view more than is really warranted by the facts. Most of the works of this type are, in fact, popular rather than critical and this explains their wide audience. In the case of these two, they are based on a fundamental misappropriation of the laws of chance and probability and in actual practice are likely to accomplish more harm than good. The data of science by their very nature are simply not designed to be bearers of such weighty "proofs." A more sober appraisal will lead us to agree with Pascal's insight mentioned earlier that of themselves the truths discovered in nature are ambiguous. They offer "too much to deny" and "too little to be sure" as far as ultimate things are concerned.[9]

Indeed, we are constrained to ask further, by what warrant does a man become a poacher of science in the misguided attempt to demonstrate rationally the existence of a God of whom the Scriptures say, "Whoever would draw near to God must *believe* that he exists"? (Hebrews 11:6, italics mine.) This is certainly one point at which we must insist that Tertullian's searching—and troublesome—question be asked: "What has Jerusalem to do with Athens?" This way of dealing wtih the matter must be rejected outright because it discredits the Christian cause in the eyes of modernity and leads Christian people to a false optimism. Misled by such "proofs," they are often unprepared when the real problem is set before them. In the long run, such attempts to "prove" the existence of God cater to the secret unbelief that is in the heart of Everyman—unbelief which stubbornly refuses to face the real truth and which cannot abide the necessity of decision.

We have had no such apologetic purpose in mind in these pages. We assume rather that a firm christological position needs no "proofs" other than those conveyed in the living encounter with God in Jesus Christ. Fortunately, truth can speak for itself and ought to need nothing more than to be clearly, relevantly stated in order to do its work. We are reminded of William Penn's observation that "truth suffers more by the heat of its defenders than from the arguments of its opposers."[10] If this is *not* God's world, no amount of logical "proving" will make it so. If, on the other hand, we are convinced that it *is* God's world, our assurance must rest on a firmer basis than that which science alone is able to supply.

Generally, we may say that when one follows the scientific approach, he asks the question: How?, while when he follows the theological approach he asks: Why? This distinction must not be made a rigid one, but it is generally correct and therefore useful.[11] There is manifestly no reason why either of these questions should rule out the other, for they clearly involve a difference of emphasis arising from different premises. It should be clear that either without the other is incomplete. Nor is there any reason why they may not be asked by the same person, for man has been endowed by his Creator with that unique and useful capacity of being able to confront reality from a variety of points of view.

In spite of the foregoing, however, we cannot believe, as Max Planck would have us, that the relationship between theology and natural science is a mere "phantom problem."[12] For the Christian thinker there can be no conflict in *principle*, for he will hold to the Augustinian assurance that all truth is ultimately God's truth. He will be the first to say that if a scientific theory or formula is based solidly upon the facts, there is no reason to believe it is not also of God. Is not the aim and ideal of science in the Christian sense the lofty notion of Kepler—to think God's thoughts after him? In the actual working out of the relationship between the two, however, we can hardly avoid some measure of controversy. Change is always painful and none more so than that which involves the adjusting of the mind to the new light that science continues to shed upon subjects upon which we have fundamental convictions and beliefs. But change hardly necessitates the abandonment of these cherished convictions. On the contrary, if the change is warranted by the consensus of scientific understanding, it follows that it must be in the direction of greater clarity and a more intelligent discipleship. It is from sympathetic, fraternal dialogue between the thought world of science and the thought world of the Christian religion that genuine progress in both knowledge and commitment can come. Diatribe has done enough damage already; dialogue holds much promise because undertaken in a spirit of good will and with a common devotion to truth.

But the situation demands more than dialogue. The way to solid progress lies in the frank recognition that the truths natural science has discovered and formulated are not only useful scientifically but that they are also essential to a Christian understanding of reality. Too long have we believed that it is possible to hold adequate Christian convictions about the world without bothering to find out what the world itself is really like.[13] Indeed, we may have labored so long under the impression that natural science and theology are "at war" with each other that we are unprepared to recognize anything more than a superficial compatibility at certain isolated points.

What science supplies is a more accurate knowledge of the ways of God. Scientific knowledge helps to make our ideas of God and his purpose for the world worthy of the Creator. It is a fact that the information gained from science can illuminate in an extraordinary measure the meaning of theological doctrines. Willard Sperry tells somewhere of a minister who every year preached a sermon on the latest advances in science. When asked why he followed this rather unusual practice, he replied, "It always gives me greatly enlarged ideas of God." If natural science can do this for us, then what is to prevent our affirming that it has a definite *Christian* function? This does not mean that we must all be scientists before we can think Christianly. Far from it. Nor does it mean that we must "invade" a territory which by right belongs to the scientist and to no other. Such compartmentalizing, as we have already suggested, is simply not tenable in a world where it has long been recognized that truth is relational in character. We cannot isolate particular truths or facts in one area of thought because they often have profound implications for other areas as well.

When the theologian gives attention to what scientists are saying about physical reality, he is likely to find that the resulting enlargement of mind contributes to enlargement of soul also, and as a consequence, to an increase of competence in carrying out the Christian task. We trust that the foregoing pages and the approach they embody will prove helpful in pointing us in the direction of a true wholeness of ministry and life as well as thought.

Indeed, is this not an essential aspect of the Church's *evangelistic* responsibility? As the thoughtful man outside the Church encounters a fruitful dialogue between Christian thinkers and sincere representatives of the world of science, conducted with the earnest intention (on the part of the Christian spokesmen) of making the message of the Bible relevant and clear, he is likely to behold in this developing wholeness a genuine invitation to that sanity which comes only in seeking the Lord.

Notes

Chapter I: The Scientific Apprehension of Reality

1. The question in itself offers sufficient material for an entire volume. Let it suffice here to refer to that basic scientific inquisitiveness first observed in the early Greek cosmologists. The scientific quest is an essential part of man's more ultimate, primary question which Emile Cailliet defines as, "What kind of place am I in?" *The Dawn of Personality,* pp. 71-72. New York: The Bobbs-Merrill Company, Inc., 1955. It was later given an ontological orientation by Parmenides, the effect of which has been in most cases destructive of true science. Cailliet terms the trend set in motion by Parmenides the "ontological deviation," that purely rational, philosophical preoccupation that hindered the mind for so long from discovering the right clue to the secrets of nature. Cf. *The Christian Approach to Culture,* pp. 131ff. Nashville: Abingdon-Cokesbury Press, 1953.

2. *Novum Organon* I, lxxvii. May be found in *The World's Great Thinkers,* Vol. IV., ed. by Saxe Commins & Robert N. Linscott, "Man and The Universe: The Philosophers of Science," p. 110. New York: Random House, 1947.

3. A helpful guide to the development of modern scientific conceptions may be found in Sir James Jeans, *The Growth of Physical Science,* Cambridge University Press, 1947, now available as a Premier Book, pub. by Fawcett World Library, New York.

4. Newton, *Opticks,* Qu. 31, quoted by Jeans, *ibid.,* p. 228.

5. There are differences of conviction among scientists regarding the relative values of experiment and mathematics in natural science. It is not our intention to enter this discussion, except to say that in our judgment both are indispensable to genuine scientific progress. Scientific experiments were performed before the modern scientific period, but their value was wasted because there was no common scientific "language" to codify and express the insights they afforded. Francis Bacon championed experiment over against Aristotle's empiricism, but even he failed to detect the remarkable correspondence between mathematical formulations and the physical world. Not until experiment and mathematics were seen to be inseparably related to each other did the sciences begin to progress—and then by leaps and bounds. Herbert Butterfield distinguishes between *experiments*—which were fairly common in ancient and medieval science—and the experimental *method* developed through the alliance of experiment with mathematics in the modern period. "The resort to experiment in the natural sciences now came (i.e., when allied with mathematics) to have direction, came at last to be organized to some purpose. For centuries it had been an affair of wild and almost pointless fluttering—a thing in many respects irrelevant to the true progress of understanding—sometimes the most capricious and fantastic part of the scientific programme." Herbert Butterfield, *The Origins of Modern Science, 1300-1800,*

p. 91. New York: The Macmillan Company, 1960. See the whole of chapter 5, "The Experimental Method in the Seventeenth Century," pp. 77-95.

6. Jeans, *op. cit.*, p. 257.

7. Fred Hoyle, in "Ultrahot Stars," *The New Astronomy*, p. 149. A Scientific-American Book. New York: Simon and Schuster, 1955. This volume contains several essays by leading scientists on various aspects of the modern astronomical perspective. See also George Gamow, *Matter, Earth, and Sky*, p. 360, Englewood Cliffs, New Jersey: Prentice-Hall, Inc., 1958, for a table of the elementary particles now known to be contained in the structure of the atom.

8. Lincoln Barnett, *The Universe and Dr. Einstein*, p. 7. New York: William Sloane Associates, second rev. edition, 1957. P. W. Bridgeman raises the interesting question, "Does nature seem to be getting intrinsically simpler as we get toward small scale phenomena?" To ordinary view, the answer would certainly seem to be affirmative. Yet Bridgeman insists that the real wonder is that there are so many laws that are simple, at least apparently, and that the "overwhelming presumption is against the laws of nature having any predisposition to simplicity as formulated in terms of our concepts." *The Logic of Modern Physics*, pp. 203-204. New York: The Macmillan Company, 1927. Paperback edition, 1960. Bridgeman recognizes that there is "great justification" for the belief that all nature will ultimately be reduced to simplicity (p. 199), but does not believe the true facts bear it out.

9. "Modern physics extends its horizons far beyond the everyday experience upon which all the 'common sense' ideas of classical physics were based, and we are thus bound to find striking deviations from our conventional way of thinking and must be prepared to encounter facts that sound quite paradoxical to our ordinary common sense," Gamow, *op. cit.*, pp. 311-312.

Chapter II: Dealing with an Obsolete Inference

1. Amos N. Wilder, *Otherworldliness and the New Testament*, pp. 22-23. New York: Harper & Brothers, 1954.

2. In his first epistle John is concerned to describe the Christian's true attitude and place in the world. The essence of the Christian ethic, he says, is love: "Beloved, let us love one another; for love is of God ..." (4:7). He reminds those who profess their love for God that "if anyone says, 'I love God,' and hates his brother, he is a liar ..." (4:20). No superficial pietism this! A thoroughgoing transformation of one's attitude toward the world and toward one's fellow human beings—this is the real proof of profession and of faith in God. Paul's great hymn of love in 1 Corinthians 13 has a similar intention. Anders Nygren suggests that Paul wrote it with the conscious purpose of offsetting the *eros* orientation toward the beautiful, the good, and the true. Cf. Anders Nygren, *Agape and Eros*, tr. by Philip S. Watson. Philadelphia: The Westminster Press, 1953 (one-volume edition).

3. Wilder, *op. cit.*, p. 23.

4. A good study of this subject is John A. T. Robinson's monograph, *The Body*, London: SCM Press, Ltd., 1952, in the series, Studies in Biblical Theology. See also in that same series, Walther Eichrodt, *Man in the Old Testament*, Chicago: Henry Regnery Company, 1951; also Rudolf Otto, *The Idea of the Holy*, pp. 95f. Oxford University Press, 1923.

5. Oscar Cullmann, *Immortality of the Soul Or Resurrection of the Dead?*, pp. 33-37. New York: The Macmillan Company, 1958.

6. John Dillenberger, "Science and Theology Today" in *The Christian Century*, Vol. 76, June 17, 1959, pp. 722-723.

7. Cullmann, *op. cit.*, p. 43.

8. We shall deal with the universal consequences of redemption in Chapter XI.

9. Cullmann, *op. cit.*, p. 15.

10. *Ibid.*, p. 37.
11. *Ibid.*, p. 41.
12. For example, the insistence that physical death and all sickness be regarded as the penalty of sin and that Christ's fear of death contrasts sharply with Socrates' calmness in drinking the hemlock, *ibid.*, pp. 19-27. The author fails to take into account the sharp differences in the circumstances of the two deaths and therefore oversimplifies the case.
13. *Ibid.*, pp. 25-26.

Chapter III: . . . And Its Corollary

1. Psalm 29 is another passage in which this vivid immediacy of God in the natural order (in this case a thunderstorm) is expressed.
2. "It is not the J writer who is immature, but the sophisticated people who have not reached an adult perception of the nature of religious symbolism and imagery." Alan Richardson, *Genesis I-XI*, p. 20. London: SCM Press, Ltd., 1953.
3. Otto, *The Idea of the Holy*, pp. 80-83.
4. *Ibid.*, p. 82.
5. Francis W. Beare, in *The Interpreter's Bible*, Vol. XI, pp. 166-167. Nashville: Abingdon Press, 1955.

Chapter IV: Physics in a New Key

1. *Physics*, Bk. II, chap. 3; may be found in *Introduction to Aristotle*, ed. by Richard McKeon, p. 122. New York: The Modern Library, 1947.
2. Herbert Butterfield describes the overcoming of the problem of motion as "the most amazing in character" and "the most stupendous in the scope of its consequences of all the intellectual hurdles" the human mind has confronted in the last fifteen hundred years. It was this because it involved the most difficult of all mental activity, namely, the breaking up of the old framework in which men understood nature and the supplying of a new framework which placed the facts in a new relation to each other. This process, Butterfield says, "virtually means putting on a different kind of thinking-cap for the moment," *The Origins of Modern Science*, Ch. I, "The Historical Importance of a Theory of Impetus," pp. 1-16. The above quotations will be found on pages 1-3. Butterfield also makes plain that the transition from the Aristotelian universe to that of Galileo was not an immediate one and that it required the endeavors of many eminent men of science. When we say therefore that the Aristotelian physics was "definitely overthrown," we are telescoping an extensive historical course of events into a single sentence. In fact, it required nearly 150 years for the transition to be made. Cf. pp. 55f.
3. William G. Pollard, *Chance and Providence*, p. 61. New York: Charles Scribner's Sons, 1958.
4. Hume uncovered the fact that in the natural world there is no necessary connection between a cause and its effect. The idea of causation is a determination of the mind; its origin is associational rather than necessary. Thus one of the basic categories of the philosophy based on Newtonian principles is discovered to have an inferential origin, and the entire view which considers knowledge as a system of necessarily connected ideas comes tumbling down. Cf. David Hume, *A Treatise of Human Nature*, ed. by T. H. Green and T. H. Grose, London, 1874, Bk. I, Part III, Sec. III, "Why a Cause Is Always Necessary."
5. Kant summarizes his formulations in the *Prolegomena to Any Future Metaphysics*. The *Prolegomena* may be found in T. V. Smith and Marjorie Grene, *From Descartes to Kant*, pp. 784-886. Chicago: The University of Chicago Press, 1933.
6. Emile Boutroux, *The Contingency of the Laws of Nature*, authorized

translation by Fred Rothwell. Chicago and London: The Open Court Publishing Company, 1920.

7. Pollard, *op. cit.*, pp. 54-56. This quotation will be found on p. 56.

8. Emile Cailliet, *The Christian Approach to Culture*, pp. 160-161. Leon Brunschvicg puts it bluntly but accurately when he says that to speak of causality at all in scientific terms amounts to saying that "there is a universe." Quoted by Emile Cailliet, *The Recovery of Purpose*, p. 31. New York: Harper & Brothers, 1959.

9. Pollard, *op. cit.*, p. 54.

10. Barnett, *The Universe and Dr. Einstein*, p. 28.

11. Albert Einstein and Leopold Infeld, *The Evolution of Physics*, p. 33. New York: Simon and Schuster, 1938.

12. In his correspondence with Lord Samuel of the Royal Institute of Philosophy in 1951. See Cailliet, *The Recovery of Purpose*, pp. 33-38, for an illuminating discussion of this exchange.

13. Barnett, *op. cit.*, p. 14.

Chapter V: A Fresh Departure for Thinking

1. *The Republic*, VI, 509—VII, 517; *Timaeus*, 28-30; *Parmenides;* in *The Dialogues of Plato*, tr. by B. Jowett, Vol. III, pp. 210-218, 352-353; Vol. IV, pp. 45-106. London: Humphrey Milford, 1931.

2. *Nichomachean Ethics*, I, 6; *Metaphysics* I, 9; III, 4; VII, 9; in *The Basic Works of Aristotle*, ed. and with an Introduction by Richard McKeon, pp. 939-941, 795-797. New York: Random House, 1941.

3. Plotinus, *Psychic and Physical Treatises; Comprising the Second and Third Enneads*, trans. by Stephen MacKenna, Ennead III, pp. 8-9, 119-141. London: Philip Lee Warner, Publishers to the Medici Society, Ltd., 1921.

4. Descartes, *Discourse on Method*, in *The Philosophical Works of Descartes*, rendered into English by E. S. Haldane and G. R. T. Ross, Vol. II, pp. 89-90. Cambridge: The University Press, 1911.

5. There are two great figures that still dominate the landscape of philosophy insofar as it has attempted a comprehensive, rational interpretation of reality. The more recent of these is Immanuel Kant, the more distant is Thomas Aquinas. Étienne Gilson correctly states that "What makes it difficult for us to go back to Thomas Aquinas is Kant. . . . But what makes it difficult for us to go as far as Kant is, if not Thomas Aquinas himself, at least the whole order of facts which provides a basis for his own natural theology." *God and Philosophy*, pp. 114-115. New Haven: Yale University Press, 1941. This is indeed true if we take as our beginning point the field of natural theology, for the Kantian formulation denies forthright any validity to the bare idea of God while Aquinas states *the* natural theology *par excellence.* The truth of the matter is, however, that modern physics now makes it impossible for us to go back—and it would be back in either case—to Kant *or* Aquinas. Since the crux of Kant's formulation is his conception of experience, and since experience to Kant is that of Newtonian science, namely, that which can be handled, measured, defined, when modern science discloses that the most determinative events go on within that area of reality most remote from experience, then it is plain that the Kantian critique is no longer applicable. Likewise, since the heart of the Thomistic scheme is a philosophical concept of existence with which authentic natural science has nothing to do, it is clear that such a philosophical framework is of no use to science. This is not to say that natural scientists do not at times attempt to state the philosophy of "a wholly mathematized science," n. 17, p. 138, but it is this attempt that frequently lands them in trouble, not the rejection of the Thomistic categories. As much as the modern world has benefited from the work of the neo-

Thomists, it should be frankly recognized that science has moved us beyond the point where we can think in any such terms of a *philosophia perennis*.

6. Einstein and Infeld characterize the evolution of physical science as "the great mystery story," *The Evolution of Physics*, p. 5.

7. Gilson, *op. cit.*, pp. 121-122.

8. Pollard, *Chance and Providence*, p. 141.

9. Einstein, Schrödinger, and de Broglie are three of the greatest modern scientists who still hold to the possibility of a return to the deterministic position, and their authority is unquestionably impressive. At the same time, it should be noted that even they admit that there is at present no experimental evidence bearing out their hope. In a particularly delicate wording of the matter de Broglie summarizes by saying, "The wisest course, no doubt, is to hold to this statement: at the present time, the physics of phenomena where quanta play a part, is no longer deterministic." Quoted by John Dillenberger, *Protestant Thought and Natural Science*, p. 274. Garden City, New York: Doubleday & Company, Inc., 1960. Two things at least ought to be said regarding the general conclusion reached in this recent able book. In the first place, even if science does discover a new deterministic facet to physical reality, it is clear that such determinism will be far removed from that of classical physics. The very complexity of quantum phenomena already makes that evident; therefore a deterministic mechanism in thought generally, that is of that obsolete variety, is extremely unlikely. For this reason it seems to me unrealistic and academic to counsel caution in exploring "extensive delineations of the interrelations of theology and science," p. 256. New dangers are undoubtedly involved, but they will be different from the old ones. And further, they are all overshadowed by the vast danger involved in leaving the matter where it now is until some future time that may be more "ripe," *ibid.* We can hardly afford to play it "safe," p. 275, when so much is at stake. In the second place, to delay the development of such a conversation between theology and natural science as we are proposing in these pages until a more favorable time (which may never come) betrays a too great emphasis on the dependence of theology upon the current state of scientific understanding. This was the error of the deists. Had they been more zealous to set forth the biblical perspective in its power and promise—even in the face of an unfavorable scientific climate—rather than seeking to accommodate theology to science, the entire course of things might have been different. The immense promise of the present is that the favorable situation in science now encourages such a positive undertaking on the part of theology. To wait until the time is more "ripe" is to suggest that what we need is a new effort like that of the deists and thus to sell the theological contribution short.

10. Quoted by L. Harold DeWolf, *The Case for Theology in Liberal Perspective*, pp. 100-101. Philadelphia: The Westminster Press, 1959.

11. The principle of complementarity has been most helpful in throwing light on many of the celebrated debates of former days. Coulson employs it to recast the basic problems of mind and matter, free-will and determinism, and teleology. Each of these debates involved points of view which were diametrically opposed to each other and which consistently cancelled out each other. Yet both of them could be substantiated in human experience itself. "Both sides are right, but they have no real contact with each other; and their points of view . . . seem to a disinterested outsider to resemble a pair of express trains traveling in opposite directions at high speed past one another, but without having any real 'contact' at all," *Science and Christian Belief*, pp. 72f. Chapel Hill, N.C.: The University of North Carolina Press, 1955. This book is by far the best I have seen dealing with the general sub-

ject. It ought to be studied as a standard text for all who are interested in the basic approach to science and its place in the Christian scheme of values.

12. Cailliet, *The Christian Approach to Culture*, pp. 144-151.

13. In fact, some scientists are now ready to abandon the notion of paradox entirely, because paradox implies that such a complementary nature of our understanding of things is an unsatisfactory and temporary expedient. "Paradox" is a term of formal logic while "complementary" in this present sense is a term of science. Cf. Pollard, *op. cit.*, pp. 151-152. "We must give up the demand that all nature be embraced in any formula, either simple or complicated. It may perhaps turn out eventually that as a matter of fact nature can be embraced in a formula, but we must so organize our thinking as not to demand it as a necessity." Bridgeman, *The Logic of Modern Physics*, p. 3.

14. Einstein, in the "Letter to Lord Samuel," quoted by Cailliet, *The Recovery of Purpose*, p. 35.

15. Einstein and Infeld, *op. cit.*, pp. 4, 30, 33. Thus Newton's insistence that no great discovery is ever made without "a bold guess." P. W. Bridgeman describes the new attitude toward scientific concepts as being "operational" in character. There is no assurance whatever that properties assumed in scientific definitions actually exist in nature; and when it is reduced to conceptual formulas and statements physics becomes just as abstract as geometry. For example, "the concept of length is . . . fixed when the operations by which length is measured are fixed; that is, the concept of length involves as much as and nothing more than the set of operations by which length is determined. In general, we mean by any concept nothing more than a set of operations; the *concept is synonymous with the corresponding set of operations*," *op. cit.*, p. 5 (italics his). If I understand Bridgeman correctly, however, he does not say that scientific concepts in themselves say little or nothing about "external nature," p. 27. He says rather that the physicist cannot concern himself with that question; the link between the concept and the external world lies in the fact that the concept itself involves physical operations and has ultimately a physical origin. Therefore in restricting statements about the behavior or nature to operations relative to a single observer the scientist is "stating something about nature," p. 27.

16. Gilson criticizes Sir James Jeans for stating that "Modern scientific theory . . . compels us to think of the creator as working outside time and space . . . just as the artist is outside his canvas," *op. cit.*, p. 125. Gilson affirms that Jeans' reasoning has nothing to do with science at all, since it is outside the immediate area of scientific investigation. At the same time, we would ask: Why cannot the scientist draw implications from his investigations if those investigations warrant? The important thing is that the scientist be honest with his hearers and confess that his implications are based on scientific presuppositions and therefore limited by those same scientific presuppositions. But when he does that, the Christian thinker ought to welcome him, not rebuff him just because he is saying what "any and every one of countless Christian theologians who knew no other world than that of Ptolemy" have said, pp. 125-126. Can we not welcome a friend?

17. A. N. Whitehead, *Science and the Modern World*, Ch. III, "The Century of Genius," pp. 39-57. The New American Library, Pelican Mentor edition, 1948.

18. Blaise Pascal, *Pensées, The Provincial Letters*, Frs. 1 and 76, pp. 3, 29. New York: The Modern Library, 1941.

19. An excellent discussion of the contribution the modern scientific outlook and Christian teaching make to each other may be found in the little volume by John Baillie, *Natural Science and the Spiritual Life*, pp. 22f. New York: Charles Scribner's Sons, 1952.

20. Cailliet, *The Recovery of Purpose*, Ch. 6, "Preliminary Words of Caution," pp. 61-69. This quotation will be found on page 69.

21. Paul Sevier Minear, in *Eyes of Faith*. Philadelphia: The Westminster Press, 1946.

22. *Ibid.*, p. 2.

23. E. J. Carnell, "Orthodoxy: Cultic vs. Classical," in *The Christian Century*, Vol. 77, March 30, 1960, p. 379.

24. See Ian Henderson, *Myth in the New Testament*, Naperville, Ill.: Alec R. Allenson, Inc., 1956 (paperback), for a summary of Bultmann's main position, as well as a helpful appraisal of it.

25. Cailliet, *The Recovery of Purpose*, pp. 58-68. Accordingly Cailliet proposes that we "de-tragicize" the Bible rather than de-mythologize it. By this he means that we rid ourselves of tragic, promethean ideas which have been imported into our Christian thinking and thereby read into the Bible. The "prophetic" view must be distinguished from the "tragic" view. Cf. the illuminating Part IV, "The Promethean Character of a Common Plight," pp. 152-160, and especially the "Conclusion," pp. 167-169.

Chapter VI: A New Open-Mindedness

1. Cf. his statement to a group of theological students: "So my advice would be that if you are faced with any such general view, you should bracket it, even if it should be called a *Christian Weltanschauung.*" Karl Barth, *Dogmatics in Outline*, tr. by G. T. Thomson, p. 60. New York: Philosophical Library, 1949. For a sympathetic appreciation of Barth's thought in this connection as in others, we must not forget the context of his revolt against a watered-down "culture-Protestantism." Barth stands in the tradition of Tertullian, Luther, and Kierkegaard in disowning any interest in a Christian world view or in Christian philosophy generally.

2. Charles Coulston Gillispie, *Genesis and Geology*. New York: Harper & Brothers, Publishers, Torchbook edition, 1959.

3. *Ibid.*, p. 30.

4. "The difficulty as reflected in scientific literature appears to be one of religion (in a crude sense) *in* science rather than one of religion *versus* science. The most embarrassing obstacles faced by the new sciences were cast up by the curious providential materialism of the scientists themselves and of those who relied upon them to show that the materials of a material universe exhibit the sort of necessity which results from control instead of the sort which springs from self-sufficiency. The work of the scientists supported a providentialist view which managed to be at the same time mundane and supernatural —mundane as to appearances and supernatural as to inferences," *ibid.*, Preface, p. ix.

5. Charles Norris Cochrane terms such a definitive given an *arché*. See *Christianity and Classical Culture*, pp. 362f. New York: Oxford University Press, 1944. Cochrane's valuable thesis in this truly great book is that Christianity won the victory over classical Graeco-Roman culture and philosophy *(Romanitas)* because it supplied a new and superior arché, a fresh starting point for interpreting and experiencing reality in all its forms.

6. "If any man's will is to do his will, he shall know whether the teaching is from God or whether I am speaking on my own authority" (John 7:17).

7. It will be instructive at this point to note the deep relationship which seems to exist between *wholeness* and *holiness*. Etymologically, the English words *whole* and *holy* are practically identical, having come from nearly the same roots *(whole* from Anglo-Saxon *hal;* and *holy* from the derivative *halig*. Cf. *Webster's New International Dictionary*, second edition, unabridged, pp. 1190 and 2921). The same basic idea, that of soundness, health, integrity of being, underlies both words. On the other hand, the dominant biblical significance of holy *(qadosh* in Hebrew and *hagios* in Greek) is that of separatedness by virtue of being consecrated to God. Strictly speaking, holiness in the biblical view belongs to God alone. Cf. the articles on "saint" and "sanctify" by

O. S. Rankin and J. K. S. Reid in *A Theological Word Book of the Bible*, edited by Alan Richardson, pp. 214-219. New York: The Macmillan Company, 1950. But this holiness is personal and can be communicated by God through revelation. In actual fact, the two ideas of holiness complement each other, for true personal integrity (wholeness) of character is fully obtainable only as a gift of the holy God. The moral character of all reality is grounded in the will of God and is realized when reality fulfills its created purpose. This too is holiness, though admittedly subordinate to the strictly religious aspect. In a later chapter we shall deal with the biblical concept of created wholeness which appears in such a text as the following from Isaiah:

> For thus says the LORD,
> who created the heavens
> (he is God!)
> who formed the earth and made it
> (he established it;
> He did not create it a chaos,
> he formed it to be inhabited!)   (45:18).

Both aspects of holiness are expressed in this text and are fully complementary.

8. Coulson, *Science and Christian Belief*, p. 87. Coulson also quotes Sir Richard Gregory, editor of *Nature:* " 'Science,' he said, 'is not to be regarded merely as a storehouse of facts to be used for material purposes, but as one of the great human endeavors to be ranked with arts and religion as the guide and expression of man's fearless quest for truth,' " p. 40.

9. *Ibid.*, p. 50.

10. *Ibid.*, p. 86.

11. Barnett, *The Universe and Dr. Einstein*, p. 105.

12. Cf., for example, the first chapter of *The Westminster Confession of Faith:* "... the light of nature, and the works of creation and providence, do so far manifest the goodness, wisdom, and power of God, as to leave men inexcusable ..." The frank acknowledgment that this general revelation in itself is not sufficient for salvation does not at all mean that it is without value.

13. I have always felt that the visit of the Magi recorded in Matthew 2 contained more meaning than customarily supposed. Babylonian astrologers they were; but did the study of the heavens in which they engaged leave them entirely in darkness? Then there is that tantalizing statement of Paul in Romans 2:14-15. Certainly we must not make the apostle say more than he intended to say. The finality of Jesus Christ is a clear New Testament teaching. Nevertheless, the implication of a wider witness is suggestive, and this is all we ourselves are willing to say at this point.

14. Cf. Cailliet, *The Recovery of Purpose*, Chs. 11 and 12, "The Wider Meaning of Revelation" and "Revelation and Degrees of Response," pp. 104-122. This is a key section for anyone interested in understanding revelation today.

15. Pascal, *Pensées*, Fr. 229, p. 78.

16. William Temple, *Nature, Man and God*, pp. 473f. New York: St. Martin's Press, 1934.

17. *Ibid.*, p. 306. Temple's argument in this chapter, "Revelation and Its Mode," should be studied in close conjunction with Cailliet's treatment of the same subject referred to above.

Chapter VII: Chance and the Purpose of God

1. In his book, *Chance and Providence*, especially ch. 4, "Chance, Time, and Miracle," pp. 89-119.

2. *Ibid.*, p. 80.

3. *Ibid.*, p. 92.
4. *Ibid.*, p. 94.
5. *Ibid.*
6. R. W. Stewart, *An Introduction to Jesus for The Twentieth Century,* pp. 119-120. New York: The Macmillan Company, 1947.
7. Cailliet, *The Recovery of Purpose,* p. 70.
8. Pollard, *op. cit.,* pp. 106-110.
9. As, for example, in a recent movie which made it appear so utterly unlikely (miraculous!) ever to have happened as even to bring discredit upon the biblical record. But it is unlikely that Hollywood will be called to account for its sensational exegesis! See Pollard, *ibid.,* where he reproduces what is probably the earliest version of the Exodus story and may reasonably be regarded as the most accurate account of it we have.
10. *Ibid.*, p. 109.
11. This analysis of the nature of providence and of man's response to it finds an unexpected echo in one of the most remarkable little volumes published in recent years. I refer to Karl Barth and Johannes Hamel, *How to Serve God in a Marxist Land.* New York: Association Press, 1959. Hamel says that the fundamental question East German Christians must face is, "Whether the Christian Church in the Marxist world openly confesses that her own Lord and Master meets her in the encounter with these powers and structures," p. 103. Here, too, it can be seen that the basic issue is a matter of perspective, of frame of reference.
12. The best guide I have found on this subject is Wade H. Boggs, Jr., *Faith Healing and the Christian Faith.* Richmond, Virginia: John Knox Press, 1956. See especially the section on "The Healing Miracles of Jesus," pp. 56-69.
13. Pollard, *op. cit.,* p. 112 (italics mine).
14. "The miracle of the exodus was never for Israel an isolated act of a God who normally was not involved in human history. It was instead forever after a clear and decisive guarantee of the providential presence of God in *every* situation," *ibid.,* p. 113 (italics mine).
15. *Ibid.*, p. 117.
16. *Ibid.*, p. 113.
17. Thus Alfred North Whitehead: "Every event on its finer side introduces God into the world," *Religion in the Making,* pp. 155-156. New York: The Macmillan Company, 1926.
18. Stewart, *op. cit.,* p. 118.
19. *Ibid.*, p. 124.
20. *Ibid.*, pp. 125-126. Since this is so, the search for the historical Jesus must ever be carried on, though on a different basis than in the theology of liberalism. Cf. in this connection D. M. Baillie, *God Was in Christ,* pp. 48-58. New York: Charles Scribner's Sons, 1948.
21. "God was never in more perfect fellowship with Jesus than in that hour of almost despairing darkness, and therefore this dying triumph of Jesus's faith demands to be interpreted as the revelation of the heart and mind of God Himself." Stewart, *op. cit.,* p. 81.

Chapter VIII: The Scientific Setting

1. Jeans, *The Growth of Physical Science,* p. 87.
2. "Indeed, we may say it was Aristotle rather than Ptolemy who had to be overthrown in the sixteenth century." Butterfield, *The Origins of Modern Science,* p. 24. Cf. further: "What was needed was a large-scale change of design—the substitution of one highly dovetailed system for another—and in a sense it appeared to be the case that the whole Aristotelian synthesis had to be overturned at once. And that is why Galileo is so important; for, at the

strategic moment, he took the lead in a policy of simultaneous attack on the whole front," p. 68.

3. Alexander Koyré, in *Moments of Discovery*, ed. by George Schwartz and Philip W. Bishop, Vol. I, *The Origins of Science*, p. 213. New York: Basic Books, Inc., 1958. See also Note 2, Ch. IV.

4. Good summaries of various aspects of contemporary astronomical knowledge by leading scientists may be found in *The New Astronomy*.

5. *Ibid.*, "The Milky Way," pp. 82-92. This quotation may be found on p. 83.

6. *Ibid.*

7. Cf. John Lear, "The Search for Intelligent Life on Other Planets," in *The Saturday Review*, January 2, 1960, pp. 39f.

8. Barnett, *The Universe and Dr. Einstein*, pp. 41, 42. We emphasize "scientifically speaking"; for some, overwhelmed by the magnitude of the modern vista, find it difficult to extend present conceptions to embrace the universe as we now understand it. E.g., E. A. Milne conceives of God as being limited by his own rationality: "The creation by God of an extended universe would require an impossibility, the impossibility of the fixation of simultaneity in the void—impossibility, that is, to a rational God. The paradox follows, that the Deity Himself . . . is yet limited by this very rationality. With God all things are not possible," cited by Coulson, *Science and Christian Belief*, pp. 18-19. In the seventeenth century, Blaise Pascal exposed the fallacy of placing such purely metaphysical, rational strictures on reality (cf. his correspondence with Father Noël about the vacuum). The same insistence must be repeated here. There is simply no place in genuine science (or religion!) for preconceived notions whose effect is to limit reality or reality's God.

Chapter IX: The Christian Setting

1. "Man Against Darkness," in *The Atlantic Monthly*, September 1948, pp. 53-58.

2. *Ibid.*, p. 54.

3. Cf. Cailliet, *The Recovery of Purpose*, pp. 24-31.

4. *Ibid.*, Ch. IV, "The Impact of Scientific Methods"; A. Cressy Morrison's *Man Does Not Stand Alone*, New York: Fleming H. Revell Company, 1944, is useful in this connection, provided the reader fastens on the evidences of purpose the author cites and does not fall victim to his attempt to prove intelligent direction and purpose. The examples Morrison cites are suggestive, if properly understood.

5. These ideas are not as recent as they might appear. In the sixteenth century Giordano Bruno, "that *enfant terrible* amongst sixteenth-century Italian speculators," spoke of a plurality of worlds and gave the scholars of his day new food for thought in the multitude of questions that sprang from this idea. Butterfield, *The Origins of Modern Science*, p. 57. Without doubt he was ahead of his time in this regard, as his untimely death at the stake bears out, but it is interesting to note that his speculations have now become scientific possibilities.

6. Pascal, *Pensées*, pp. 21-22.

7. Sir James Jeans, quoted by Barnett, *The Universe and Dr. Einstein*, p. 93. Cf. also George Gamow, *The Birth and Death of the Sun*, A Mentor Book, pub. by The New American Library, 1952, especially Ch. 12, "The Birth of the Universe," pp. 195-202.

8. The reader is referred to an excellent set of lectures by Prof. Edward McCrady of Sewanee (University of the South), the first of which summarizes the evidence for the beginning. These lectures in the "Episcopal Churchmen

Series" are on tape at the Reigner Recording Library, Union Theological Seminary, Richmond, Virginia, and are available on loan. McCrady sets the age of the earth at around 5 billion years, while Gamow adds, "Plus or minus five per cent." The most recent calculations place the age of the universe at around 10 billion years, four billion years older than generally thought even a few years ago. The new estimate was made by Dr. Fred Hoyle of St. John's College, Cambridge, using an IBM 704 computer. Such changes indicate that the situation is still in a state of considerable flux.

9. A good discussion of the two views may be found in "Modern Cosmology," by Gamow in *The New Astronomy*, pp. 3-24.

10. Dante Alighieri, "The Divine Comedy," quoted in *Masterpieces of Religious Verse*, ed. by James Dalton Morrison, p. 5. New York: Harper & Brothers, 1948.

Chapter X: A Basic Compatibility

1. Langdon Gilkey, *Maker of Heaven and Earth*, p. 263, n. 18. Garden City, New York: Doubleday & Company, Inc., 1959. This is the most up-to-date and adequate volume available today on the doctrine of creation.

2. Charles E. Raven, *Science and the Christian Man*, p. 34. New York: The Macmillan Company (paperback), first published 1952. Canon Raven points out that Milton, Hobbes, and Newton would all have shared the belief that the world was about 5600 years old and that it was created in substantially its present form.

3. William M. Logan, *In the Beginning God*, p. 15. Richmond, Virginia: John Knox Press, 1957.

4. Alan Richardson, *Genesis I-XI*, p. 28.

5. Logan, *op. cit.*, pp. 15-16.

6. *Ibid.*, p. 13.

7. Richardson, *op. cit.*, p. 43.

8. C. N. Cochrane points out that part of the real power of the early Church lay in its doctrine of creation. The biblical faith supplied the solution to the vexing question of how God could impart real existence to other beings whose existence was not of the nature of God himself. The only solution *Romanitas* could supply was to say that reality came into being by emanation from God. But this inevitably made for a pantheistic world, blurring the distinction between Creator and creature and failing to account for the uniqueness of human personality. In the Christian perspective, God's operations in creation and redemption form the constituent events in the Christian doctrine of time as meaningful duration and led to the formulation of the Christian philosophy of history as the stage on which God's purpose is being enacted. Cf. *Christianity and Classical Culture*, pp. 403, 410f.

9. Gilkey, *op. cit.*, p. 32.

10. Coulson, *Science and Christian Belief*, p. 30.

11. *Ibid.*, pp. 19, 20.

12. Published by the National Council of the Episcopal Church, 281 Fourth Avenue, New York 10, New York.

13. *Ibid.*, p. 13.

14. *Ibid.*, p. 16.

15. *Ibid.*, p. 21.

16. *Ibid.*, pp. 17-25.

17. *Ibid.*, p. 26.

Chapter XI: Invitation to Sanity

1. Chapter III.

2. The best treatment of this theme I have found is the volume by C. W. Quimby, *The Jubilant Year*. Nashville: Abingdon-Cokesbury Press, 1946.

Such a book exhibits the genuine, biblical exuberance and sense of wonder that accompany the joyful response to God of the Christian living in God's world.

3. Gilkey, *Maker of Heaven and Earth*, p. 16.

4. *Ibid.*, pp. 211, 212.

5. In *The Interpreter's Bible*, Vol. VIII, p. 453. Cf. Brooke Foss Westcott, *The Gospel According to St. John*, pp. xxxii-xxxix. London: John Murray, 1908. Westcott detects two strains in Philo's use of Logos: the *Word (Memra)*, and the *Reason*. The former is Hebraic and the latter the Greek term; the author states categorically that "the teaching of St. John is characteristically Hebraic and not Alexandrine," p. xxxix.

6. Charles E. Raven, *Christianity and Science*, p. 58. New York: Association Press, 1955.

7. *Ibid.*, ch. 8, "The Love of God," pp. 68-77.

8. Cf. Gamow, *The Birth and Death of the Sun*, Chs. 5, 8, 9, pp. 89-106, 140-170.

9. See, e.g., 2 Thessalonians 2 and 3.

10. Cf. Beare in *The Interpreter's Bible*, Vol. X, p. 621.

11. Quoted by John C. Bennett, "What Can We Hope For in Society?", in *What the Christian Hopes for in Society*, ed. by Wayne H. Cowan, Ch. 1, p. 34. New York: Association Press, 1957.

Conclusion

1. A good treatment of this interesting subject is Bertrand Russell's, *The Impact of Science Upon Society*. New York: Simon and Schuster, 1953.

2. James Denney, *Studies in Theology*, p. 7. New York: A. C. Armstrong and Son, 1895. Cf. further: "The result which follows from the contempt with which . . . philosophical arguments are treated by most of Ritschl's school, is not that theology is kept more purely Christian, but that it loses in solidity and in objective value," p. 5.

3. Harold DeWolf has a good summary section on the various efforts made by Christian thinkers to deal with the world of culture, citing especially their dangers, *The Case for Theology in Liberal Perspective*, pp. 57-59. "The legitimate task of the Christian thinker is clearly to enter into genuine communication with the culture of his day, but to keep himself steeped in the historic teachings of the Bible and Church," p. 59.

4. Cf. Cailliet, *The Dawn of Personality*, p. 118, for the pattern of this retreat.

5. Coulson, *Science and Christian Belief*, p. 20. The adroit shadow boxing in which N. H. Ridderbos engages in his book, *Is There a Conflict Between Genesis 1 and Natural Science?* (Grand Rapids, Michigan: Wm. B. Eerdman's Publishing Co., 1957) leaves the reader wondering just what the author takes to be the answer to the question he has posed. He nowhere deals with what science affirms about the creative process, yet he insists that Genesis "makes pronouncements which lie squarely within the field of natural sciences," p. 23. I assume he means by these "pronouncements" the idea that the human race has a "single ancestral head," p. 22. But nowhere does he discuss what this might mean for science itself. He says the Bible contains "normative" data for the natural and other sciences, p. 24; yet he nowhere discusses these data in a scientific context. One can only conclude that he is uninterested in what science says; therefore his work in this book hardly qualifies as an adequate answer to the question the title presents. Such ivory tower theologizing can only intensify the conflict the author seeks to end. But it is, sadly enough, not untypical of some attempts to iron out differences between theology and science.

6. In all too many cases theological formulations are simply restatements of traditional doctrinal positions. They follow the presuppositions of particular theologians, the orientation of the contemporary mind, or points of view of older schools of thought that persist into the present. The theological revival of recent times has not eliminated the distasteful practice of "labeling" Christian thinkers. Though there has been a reshuffling of the lines, we still speak quite commonly of "liberals," "conservatives," and the like; and the most influential of the modern theological schools has earned itself a new label, that of "neo-orthodox." The newest of the schools, the "neo-conservative," may not unfairly be regarded as a new theological model produced to replace an older product generally discredited during the fundamentalist struggles of the twenties and thirties. It goes without saying, of course, that those included in these designations are giving voice to some emphasis or facet of the whole Christian message which is valid and important. At least this is true in most cases. But it is also true that a great deal of effort is wasted in prideful partisanship. Worst of all, there is the fact that in the concern to express "the way it seems to me," or "the way our camp sees it," the cutting edge of the Christian message in the contemporary world is considerably dulled, and the Christian cause suffers thereby.

7. Lecomte Du Nouy, *Human Destiny*, p. 12. A Signet Book, The New American Library, 1947.

8. Morrison, *Man Does Not Stand Alone*, p. 13.

9. Pascal, *Pensées*, Fr. 229, p. 78. Pascal's antithesis here is not only characteristically succinct; it is also characteristically precise. It exposes the error which has colored even scholarly attempts to deal with the problem of theology and natural science. This is the error of conceiving the two as being sets of knowledge or truth existing *on the same level;* and, having done so, to set about determining how the two can be related, i.e., how the convictions held by the one can be "reconciled" with those of the other, or used to "support" the convictions of the other, or in some cases how these convictions can be "defended" against those of the other. In all likelihood, this basically academic, detached way of looking at it is the way the generality of people regard the problem. But truth does not exist "all on one level," as it were; it is hierarchical in structure, and the facts and figures gained at a lower level can be illuminated by viewing them from the vantage point of a higher level (or, as Pascal would put it, from a higher "order"—see, e.g., Fr. 792 of the *Pensées*, truly a splendid summary of the basic structure of truth). Scientific processes in themselves do not supply theological meaning, nor should they be expected to. Theologians must not be asked to wait on tomorrow's experiments to know if their deepest convictions are true or not. If theological meaning needs to be secured from other than theological sources, something is radically wrong with the theology. Nor should theologians try to inject theological meaning into science. Even a brief survey of the history of the problem of theology and science will reveal the peril of this course. Theology and natural science will never be satisfactorily "related" in this academic fashion, for the reason that such a method ignores the fact of *involvement.*

10. Quoted by Cailliet, *The Dawn of Personality*, p. 174.

11. Burnett Hillman Streeter expresses this same basic distinction by suggesting that science deals with the question of quantity and religion with that of quality. Science gives a representation of reality which is like a diagram, while religion represents it as a picture. Streeter's view, therefore, is that science and religion stand for two complementary methods by which man apprehends the nature of reality. Cf. *Reality, A New Correlation of Science and Religion*, pp. 30-31. New York: The Macmillan Company, 1926.

12. Quoted by Coulson, *op. cit.*, p. 31.

13. Karl Barth is at least consistent in affirming that "with respect to what Holy Scripture and the Christian Church understand by God's work of creation, there can be absolutely no questions, objections, or aids from the side of natural science." (Quoted by Ridderbos, *op. cit.*, pp. 23, 24). Barth's intention is to exalt Scripture, and he does not hesitate to do so, even at the expense of science and at the risk of virtually deifying the theologian. Yet such dogmatism fails in its intention for the precise reason that Scripture reveals God to be the Creator of all things. The theologian therefore has no choice but to inform himself on what science says about the creative process. The overall effect of Barth's view (to quote Denney again) is "not that theology is kept more purely Christian, but that it loses in solidity and in objective value," cf. note 2.

Index